Aroma Freedom Technique Session & Affirmation Pocket Journal

~ a companion to the book
The Aroma Freedom Technique

52 Sessions

created by Angie Taylor
Certified Aroma Freedom Technique Practitioner

I love that life is a journey! More importantly it's a never ending adventure that takes us through twists and turns that stretch us further than we ever imagined. The things we have the opportunity to learn about ourselves on a daily basis is truly inspiring and, for far too many, frightening.

Aroma Freedom Technique, created by Dr. Benjamin Perkus, gives us all a way to truly enjoy the journey and look forward to every adventure that life throws our way. Using essential oils to quickly release limiting beliefs that have a root in past emotional events gives each one of us the real gift of unleashing the God-given purpose we have held deep inside since our moment of birth.

I created this *Aroma Freedom Technique* (AFT) *Session & Affirmation Journal* so you have a place to keep track of your journey and adventures. The very first page is where you can keep a running list of things you want to work on as it's highly satisfying to check off what we have accomplished. The remaining pages are for you to use as you take yourself through an AFT session followed by the affirmation and daily anchoring routine. When you're ready to move forward, simply turn the page and begin to fill in each area.

Always remember that there is a growing list of Certified AFT Practitioners at **www.AromaFreedom.com** in case you get stuck and need some guidance. We are here to support you along your journey and be your guide as you move through the adventures on which your life's path takes you.

Are you ready to start your journey? Hang on for the adventure of a lifetime!!

Angie Taylor

1

What I Want in Life

_____
_____
_____
_____
_____
_____
_____
_____
_____
_____
_____
_____
_____
_____
_____
_____
_____
_____
_____
_____
_____
_____
_____
_____
_____
_____
_____
_____

Date of Personal AFT Session: _____

Step 1 - Set Your Intention: _____

_____

Rating your intention. How possible does it feel? (Circle One)

    Zero Hope - 0 1 2 3 4 5 6 7 8 9 10 - Absolute Confidence

Step 2 - What does the negative voice say that tells you this is not possible? _____

_____

Step 3 - How do you feel when you hear this negative voice (find ONE word)? _____

Step 4 - Where do you feel this in your body? _____

_____

Step 5 - Drift back to an earlier time when you felt the same way - get a snapshot or a movie. (Circle One)

    Snapshot   Movie   No Image

Notes on previous memory _____

_____

Step 6 - Smell Memory Release Blend or other oils - specify which oils used: _____

Step 7 - Notice changes: _____

_____

Step 8 - Is there a new belief or mindset that has emerged? _____

_____

Step 9 - Read the original intention and rate it again - how possible does it feel now? (circle one)

    Zero Hope - 0 1 2 3 4 5 6 7 8 9 10 - Absolute Confidence

(If 8 or higher (or if no negative voice), skip to Step 10 - the Affirmation. If less than 8, return to Step 2 on next page.)

How far have you shifted thus far?

        Starting number: _____ New Number: _____

Step 2 - Re-read the intention and listen for what else the negative voice says about why it can't happen. _____

Step 3 - How do you feel when you hear the negative voice? (find ONE word) _____

Step 4 - Where do you feel this in your body? _____

_____

Step 5 - Drift back to an earlier time when you felt the same way - get a snapshot or a movie. (Circle One)

        Snapshot   Movie   No Image

Notes on previous memory: _____

_____

Step 6 - Smell Memory Release Blend or other oils - specify which oils used: _____

Step 7 - Notice changes _____

_____

Step 8 - Is there a new belief or mindset that has emerged? _____

_____

Step 9 - Read the original intention and rate it again - how possible does it feel now? (circle)

        Zero Hope - 0 1 2 3 4 5 6 7 8 9 10 - Absolute Confidence

Look how far you've shifted!

        Starting number: _____ Second Number: _____

                Final Number: _____

(Move forward to Step 10 - the Affirmation - even if you're not yet at an 8 or higher. More shifting will occur during the next 3 steps.)

Step 10 - Affirmation: _____

_____
_____
_____

Step 11 - Stand in Power Pose: Repeat the affirmation for 2 minutes, twice daily, with conviction while standing in a power pose. Smell *Believe*™ or *Transformation*™ Oil Blend as you do this. (You may choose another transforming oil if you'd like, such as *Build Your Dream*™, *Magnify Your Purpose*™, etc)

Repeat for *at least three consecutive days*, or until you create a new affirmation. Check off each box when complete.

Always make sure that your energy feels clear when you say the statement. If you experience inner resistance, use the AFT process to identify and release any negative thoughts, feelings, or memories that come up.

Date	AM	PM

Step 12 - Make Your Plan of Action: _____

_____
_____
_____
_____
_____
_____

Follow-up - What has changed in your life because of THIS Aroma Freedom Technique Session? _____

_____

_____

_____

_____

_____

_____

_____

_____

_____

_____

_____

_____

_____

_____

_____

_____

_____

_____

_____

Program your mind daily! As soon as one affirmation is complete or the goal has been reached, create another. Make affirmations a daily habit and soon you will not feel right unless you have done your daily practice. This will keep you focused in the direction of your dreams. Feel free to experiment with different oils as you progress.

Date of Personal AFT Session: _____

Step 1 - Set Your Intention: _____

_____

Rating your intention. How possible does it feel? (Circle One)

Zero Hope - 0 1 2 3 4 5 6 7 8 9 10 - Absolute Confidence

Step 2 - What does the negative voice say that tells you this is not possible? _____

_____

Step 3 - How do you feel when you hear this negative voice (find ONE word)? _____

Step 4 - Where do you feel this in your body? _____

Step 5 - Drift back to an earlier time when you felt the same way - get a snapshot or a movie. (Circle One)

Snapshot   Movie   No Image

Notes on previous memory _____

_____

Step 6 - Smell Memory Release Blend or other oils - specify which oils used: _____

Step 7 - Notice changes: _____

_____

Step 8 - Is there a new belief or mindset that has emerged? _____

_____

Step 9 - Read the original intention and rate it again - how possible does it feel now? (circle one)

Zero Hope - 0 1 2 3 4 5 6 7 8 9 10 - Absolute Confidence

(If 8 or higher (or if no negative voice), skip to Step 10 - the Affirmation. If less than 8, return to Step 2 on next page.)

9

How far have you shifted thus far?

        Starting number: _____ New Number: _____

Step 2 - Re-read the intention and listen for what else the negative voice says about why it can't happen. _____

_____

Step 3 - How do you feel when you hear the negative voice? (find ONE word) _____

Step 4 - Where do you feel this in your body? _____

_____

Step 5 - Drift back to an earlier time when you felt the same way - get a snapshot or a movie. (Circle One)

        Snapshot   Movie   No Image

Notes on previous memory: _____

_____

Step 6 - Smell Memory Release Blend or other oils - specify which oils used: _____

Step 7 - Notice changes _____

_____

Step 8 - Is there a new belief or mindset that has emerged? _____

_____

Step 9 - Read the original intention and rate it again - how possible does it feel now? (circle)

    Zero Hope - 0 1 2 3 4 5 6 7 8 9 10 - Absolute Confidence

Look how far you've shifted!

        Starting number: _____ Second Number: _____

              Final Number: _____

(Move forward to Step 10 - the Affirmation - even if you're not yet at an 8 or higher. More shifting will occur during the next 3 steps.)

10

Step 10 - Affirmation: _____

_____

_____

_____

Step 11 - Stand in Power Pose: Repeat the affirmation for 2 minutes, twice daily, with conviction while standing in a power pose. Smell *Believe*™ or *Transformation*™ Oil Blend as you do this. (You may choose another transforming oil if you'd like, such as *Build Your Dream*™, *Magnify Your Purpose*™, etc)

Repeat for <u>*at least three consecutive days*</u>, or until you create a new affirmation. Check off each box when complete.

Always make sure that your energy feels clear when you say the statement. If you experience inner resistance, use the AFT process to identify and release any negative thoughts, feelings, or memories that come up.

Date	AM	PM

Step 12 - Make Your Plan of Action: _____

_____

_____

_____

_____

11

Follow-up - What has changed in your life because of THIS Aroma Freedom Technique Session? _____

_____

_____

_____

_____

_____

_____

_____

_____

_____

_____

_____

_____

_____

_____

_____

_____

_____

_____

Program your mind daily! As soon as one affirmation is complete or the goal has been reached, create another. Make affirmations a daily habit and soon you will not feel right unless you have done your daily practice. This will keep you focused in the direction of your dreams. Feel free to experiment with different oils as you progress.

Date of Personal AFT Session: _____

Step 1 - Set Your Intention: _____
_____
_____

Rating your intention. How possible does it feel? (Circle One)

     Zero Hope - 0 1 2 3 4 5 6 7 8 9 10 - Absolute Confidence

Step 2 - What does the negative voice say that tells you this is not possible? _____
_____

Step 3 - How do you feel when you hear this negative voice (find ONE word)? _____

Step 4 - Where do you feel this in your body? _____
_____

Step 5 - Drift back to an earlier time when you felt the same way - get a snapshot or a movie. (Circle One)

     Snapshot   Movie   No Image

Notes on previous memory _____
_____
_____

Step 6 - Smell Memory Release Blend or other oils - specify which oils used: _____

Step 7 - Notice changes: _____
_____
_____

Step 8 - Is there a new belief or mindset that has emerged? _____
_____
_____

Step 9 - Read the original intention and rate it again - how possible does it feel now? (circle one)

     Zero Hope - 0 1 2 3 4 5 6 7 8 9 10 - Absolute Confidence

(If 8 or higher (or if no negative voice), skip to Step 10 - the Affirmation. If less than 8, return to Step 2 on next page.)

How far have you shifted thus far?

Starting number: _____ New Number: _____

Step 2 - Re-read the intention and listen for what else the negative voice says about why it can't happen. _____

_____

Step 3 - How do you feel when you hear the negative voice? (find ONE word) _____

Step 4 - Where do you feel this in your body? _____

_____

Step 5 - Drift back to an earlier time when you felt the same way - get a snapshot or a movie. (Circle One)

        Snapshot   Movie   No Image

Notes on previous memory: _____

_____

Step 6 - Smell Memory Release Blend or other oils - specify which oils used: _____

Step 7 - Notice changes _____

_____

Step 8 - Is there a new belief or mindset that has emerged? _____

_____

Step 9 - Read the original intention and rate it again - how possible does it feel now? (circle)

    Zero Hope - 0 1 2 3 4 5 6 7 8 9 10 - Absolute Confidence

Look how far you've shifted!

Starting number: _____ Second Number: _____

Final Number: _____

(Move forward to Step 10 - the Affirmation - even if you're not yet at an 8 or higher. More shifting will occur during the next 3 steps.)

14

Step 10 - Affirmation: _____

_____

_____

_____

Step 11 - Stand in Power Pose: Repeat the affirmation for 2 minutes, twice daily, with conviction while standing in a power pose. Smell *Believe*™ or *Transformation*™ Oil Blend as you do this. (You may choose another transforming oil if you'd like, such as *Build Your Dream*™, *Magnify Your Purpose*™, etc)

Repeat for _at least three consecutive days_, or until you create a new affirmation. Check off each box when complete.

Always make sure that your energy feels clear when you say the statement. If you experience inner resistance, use the AFT process to identify and release any negative thoughts, feelings, or memories that come up.

Date	AM	PM

Step 12 - Make Your Plan of Action: _____

_____

_____

_____

_____

_____

Follow-up - What has changed in your life because of THIS Aroma Freedom Technique Session? _____

_____
_____
_____
_____
_____
_____
_____
_____
_____
_____
_____
_____
_____
_____
_____
_____
_____
_____
_____

Program your mind daily! As soon as one affirmation is complete or the goal has been reached, create another. Make affirmations a daily habit and soon you will not feel right unless you have done your daily practice. This will keep you focused in the direction of your dreams. Feel free to experiment with different oils as you progress.

Date of Personal AFT Session: _____

Step 1 - Set Your Intention: _____
_____
_____

Rating your intention. How possible does it feel? (Circle One)

    Zero Hope - 0 1 2 3 4 5 6 7 8 9 10 - Absolute Confidence

Step 2 - What does the negative voice say that tells you this is not possible? _____
_____

Step 3 - How do you feel when you hear this negative voice (find ONE word)? _____

Step 4 - Where do you feel this in your body? _____

Step 5 - Drift back to an earlier time when you felt the same way - get a snapshot or a movie. (Circle One)

    Snapshot   Movie   No Image

Notes on previous memory _____
_____
_____

Step 6 - Smell Memory Release Blend or other oils - specify which oils used: _____

Step 7 - Notice changes: _____
_____
_____

Step 8 - Is there a new belief or mindset that has emerged? _____
_____
_____

Step 9 - Read the original intention and rate it again - how possible does it feel now? (circle one)

    Zero Hope - 0 1 2 3 4 5 6 7 8 9 10 - Absolute Confidence

(If 8 or higher (or if no negative voice), skip to Step 10 - the Affirmation. If less than 8, return to Step 2 on next page.)

17

How far have you shifted thus far?

           Starting number: _____ New Number: _____

Step 2 - Re-read the intention and listen for what else the negative voice says about why it can't happen. _____

_____

Step 3 - How do you feel when you hear the negative voice? (find ONE word) _____

Step 4 - Where do you feel this in your body? _____

_____

Step 5 - Drift back to an earlier time when you felt the same way - get a snapshot or a movie. (Circle One)

        Snapshot   Movie   No Image

Notes on previous memory: _____

_____

Step 6 - Smell Memory Release Blend or other oils - specify which oils used: _____

Step 7 - Notice changes _____

_____

Step 8 - Is there a new belief or mindset that has emerged? _____

_____

Step 9 - Read the original intention and rate it again - how possible does it feel now? (circle)

      Zero Hope - 0 1 2 3 4 5 6 7 8 9 10 - Absolute Confidence

Look how far you've shifted!

        Starting number: _____ Second Number: _____

                Final Number: _____

(Move forward to Step 10 - the Affirmation - even if you're not yet at an 8 or higher. More shifting will occur during the next 3 steps.)

Step 10 - Affirmation: _____

_____
_____
_____

Step 11 - Stand in Power Pose: Repeat the affirmation for 2 minutes, twice daily, with conviction while standing in a power pose. Smell *Believe*™ or *Transformation*™ Oil Blend as you do this. (You may choose another transforming oil if you'd like, such as *Build Your Dream*™, *Magnify Your Purpose*™, etc)

Repeat for *at least three consecutive days,* or until you create a new affirmation. Check off each box when complete.

Always make sure that your energy feels clear when you say the statement. If you experience inner resistance, use the AFT process to identify and release any negative thoughts, feelings, or memories that come up.

Date	AM	PM

Step 12 - Make Your Plan of Action: _____

_____
_____
_____
_____
_____
_____

Follow-up - What has changed in your life because of THIS Aroma Freedom Technique Session? _____

_____
_____
_____
_____
_____
_____
_____
_____
_____
_____
_____
_____
_____
_____
_____
_____
_____
_____
_____

Program your mind daily! As soon as one affirmation is complete or the goal has been reached, create another. Make affirmations a daily habit and soon you will not feel right unless you have done your daily practice. This will keep you focused in the direction of your dreams. Feel free to experiment with different oils as you progress.

Date of Personal AFT Session: _____

Step 1 - Set Your Intention: _____
_____

Rating your intention. How possible does it feel? (Circle One)

     Zero Hope - 0 1 2 3 4 5 6 7 8 9 10 - Absolute Confidence

Step 2 - What does the negative voice say that tells you this is not possible? _____
_____

Step 3 - How do you feel when you hear this negative voice (find ONE word)? _____

Step 4 - Where do you feel this in your body? _____
_____

Step 5 - Drift back to an earlier time when you felt the same way - get a snapshot or a movie. (Circle One)

     Snapshot   Movie   No Image

Notes on previous memory _____
_____
_____

Step 6 - Smell Memory Release Blend or other oils - specify which oils used: _____

Step 7 - Notice changes: _____
_____
_____

Step 8 - Is there a new belief or mindset that has emerged? _____
_____

Step 9 - Read the original intention and rate it again - how possible does it feel now? (circle one)

     Zero Hope - 0 1 2 3 4 5 6 7 8 9 10 - Absolute Confidence

(If 8 or higher (or if no negative voice), skip to Step 10 - the Affirmation. If less than 8, return to Step 2 on next page.)

21

How far have you shifted thus far?

Starting number: _____ New Number: _____

Step 2 - Re-read the intention and listen for what else the negative voice says about why it can't happen. _____

_____

Step 3 - How do you feel when you hear the negative voice? (find ONE word) _____

Step 4 - Where do you feel this in your body? _____

_____

Step 5 - Drift back to an earlier time when you felt the same way - get a snapshot or a movie. (Circle One)

Snapshot   Movie   No Image

Notes on previous memory: _____

_____

Step 6 - Smell Memory Release Blend or other oils - specify which oils used: _____

Step 7 - Notice changes _____

_____

Step 8 - Is there a new belief or mindset that has emerged? _____

_____

Step 9 - Read the original intention and rate it again - how possible does it feel now? (circle)

Zero Hope - 0 1 2 3 4 5 6 7 8 9 10 - Absolute Confidence

Look how far you've shifted!

Starting number: _____ Second Number: _____

Final Number: _____

(Move forward to Step 10 - the Affirmation - even if you're not yet at an 8 or higher. More shifting will occur during the next 3 steps.)

Step 10 - Affirmation: _____

_____
_____
_____

Step 11 - Stand in Power Pose: Repeat the affirmation for 2 minutes, twice daily, with conviction while standing in a power pose. Smell _Believe_™ or _Transformation_™ Oil Blend as you do this. (You may choose another transforming oil if you'd like, such as _Build Your Dream_™, _Magnify Your Purpose_™, etc)

Repeat for _at least three consecutive days_, or until you create a new affirmation. Check off each box when complete.

Always make sure that your energy feels clear when you say the statement. If you experience inner resistance, use the AFT process to identify and release any negative thoughts, feelings, or memories that come up.

Date	AM	PM

Step 12 - Make Your Plan of Action: _____

_____
_____
_____
_____
_____
_____

Follow-up - What has changed in your life because of THIS Aroma Freedom Technique Session? _____

_____

_____

_____

_____

_____

_____

_____

_____

_____

_____

_____

_____

_____

_____

_____

_____

_____

_____

_____

Program your mind daily! As soon as one affirmation is complete or the goal has been reached, create another. Make affirmations a daily habit and soon you will not feel right unless you have done your daily practice. This will keep you focused in the direction of your dreams. Feel free to experiment with different oils as you progress.

Date of Personal AFT Session: _____

Step 1 - Set Your Intention: _____
_____
_____

Rating your intention. How possible does it feel? (Circle One)

    Zero Hope - 0 1 2 3 4 5 6 7 8 9 10 - Absolute Confidence

Step 2 - What does the negative voice say that tells you this is not possible? _____
_____

Step 3 - How do you feel when you hear this negative voice (find ONE word)? _____

Step 4 - Where do you feel this in your body? _____

Step 5 - Drift back to an earlier time when you felt the same way - get a snapshot or a movie. (Circle One)

    Snapshot   Movie   No Image

Notes on previous memory _____
_____
_____

Step 6 - Smell Memory Release Blend or other oils - specify which oils used: _____

Step 7 - Notice changes: _____
_____
_____

Step 8 - Is there a new belief or mindset that has emerged? _____
_____
_____

Step 9 - Read the original intention and rate it again - how possible does it feel now? (circle one)

    Zero Hope - 0 1 2 3 4 5 6 7 8 9 10 - Absolute Confidence

(If 8 or higher (or if no negative voice), skip to Step 10 - the Affirmation. If less than 8, return to Step 2 on next page.)

How far have you shifted thus far?

Starting number: _____ New Number: _____

Step 2 - Re-read the intention and listen for what else the negative voice says about why it can't happen. _____

_____

Step 3 - How do you feel when you hear the negative voice? (find ONE word) _____

Step 4 - Where do you feel this in your body? _____

_____

Step 5 - Drift back to an earlier time when you felt the same way - get a snapshot or a movie. (Circle One)

Snapshot   Movie   No Image

Notes on previous memory: _____

_____

Step 6 - Smell Memory Release Blend or other oils - specify which oils used: _____

Step 7 - Notice changes _____

_____

Step 8 - Is there a new belief or mindset that has emerged? _____

_____

Step 9 - Read the original intention and rate it again - how possible does it feel now? (circle)

Zero Hope - 0 1 2 3 4 5 6 7 8 9 10 - Absolute Confidence

Look how far you've shifted!

Starting number: _____ Second Number: _____

Final Number: _____

(Move forward to Step 10 - the Affirmation - even if you're not yet at an 8 or higher. More shifting will occur during the next 3 steps.)

Step 10 - Affirmation: _____

_____

_____

_____

Step 11 - Stand in Power Pose: Repeat the affirmation for 2 minutes, twice daily, with conviction while standing in a power pose. Smell *Believe*™ or *Transformation*™ Oil Blend as you do this. (You may choose another transforming oil if you'd like, such as *Build Your Dream*™, *Magnify Your Purpose*™, etc)

Repeat for _at least three consecutive days_, or until you create a new affirmation. Check off each box when complete.

Always make sure that your energy feels clear when you say the statement. If you experience inner resistance, use the AFT process to identify and release any negative thoughts, feelings, or memories that come up.

Date	AM	PM

Step 12 - Make Your Plan of Action: _____

_____

_____

_____

_____

_____

_____

Follow-up - What has changed in your life because of THIS Aroma Freedom Technique Session? _____

_____

_____

_____

_____

_____

_____

_____

_____

_____

_____

_____

_____

_____

_____

_____

_____

_____

_____

Program your mind daily! As soon as one affirmation is complete or the goal has been reached, create another. Make affirmations a daily habit and soon you will not feel right unless you have done your daily practice. This will keep you focused in the direction of your dreams. Feel free to experiment with different oils as you progress.

Date of Personal AFT Session: _____

Step 1 - Set Your Intention: _____

_____

Rating your intention. How possible does it feel? (Circle One)

Zero Hope - 0 1 2 3 4 5 6 7 8 9 10 - Absolute Confidence

Step 2 - What does the negative voice say that tells you this is not possible? _____

Step 3 - How do you feel when you hear this negative voice (find ONE word)? _____

Step 4 - Where do you feel this in your body? _____

Step 5 - Drift back to an earlier time when you felt the same way - get a snapshot or a movie. (Circle One)

Snapshot   Movie   No Image

Notes on previous memory _____

_____

Step 6 - Smell Memory Release Blend or other oils - specify which oils used: _____

Step 7 - Notice changes: _____

_____

Step 8 - Is there a new belief or mindset that has emerged? _____

_____

Step 9 - Read the original intention and rate it again - how possible does it feel now? (circle one)

Zero Hope - 0 1 2 3 4 5 6 7 8 9 10 - Absolute Confidence

(If 8 or higher (or if no negative voice), skip to Step 10 - the Affirmation. If less than 8, return to Step 2 on next page.)

How far have you shifted thus far?

　　　　　Starting number: _____ New Number: _____

Step 2 - Re-read the intention and listen for what else the negative voice says about why it can't happen. _____

_____

Step 3 - How do you feel when you hear the negative voice? (find ONE word) _____

Step 4 - Where do you feel this in your body? _____

_____

Step 5 - Drift back to an earlier time when you felt the same way - get a snapshot or a movie. (Circle One)

　　　　Snapshot　　　Movie　　　No Image

Notes on previous memory: _____

_____

Step 6 - Smell Memory Release Blend or other oils - specify which oils used: _____

Step 7 - Notice changes _____

_____

Step 8 - Is there a new belief or mindset that has emerged? _____

_____

Step 9 - Read the original intention and rate it again - how possible does it feel now? (circle)

　　　Zero Hope - 0 1 2 3 4 5 6 7 8 9 10 - Absolute Confidence

Look how far you've shifted!

　　　　　Starting number: _____ Second Number: _____
　　　　　　　　Final Number: _____

(Move forward to Step 10 - the Affirmation - even if you're not yet at an 8 or higher. More shifting will occur during the next 3 steps.)

Step 10 - Affirmation: _____

_____

_____

Step 11 - Stand in Power Pose: Repeat the affirmation for 2 minutes, twice daily, with conviction while standing in a power pose. Smell *Believe*™ or *Transformation*™ Oil Blend as you do this. (You may choose another transforming oil if you'd like, such as *Build Your Dream*™, *Magnify Your Purpose*™, etc)

Repeat for <u>at least three consecutive days</u>, or until you create a new affirmation. Check off each box when complete.

Always make sure that your energy feels clear when you say the statement. If you experience inner resistance, use the AFT process to identify and release any negative thoughts, feelings, or memories that come up.

Date	AM	PM

Step 12 - Make Your Plan of Action: _____

_____

_____

_____

_____

_____

31

Follow-up - What has changed in your life because of THIS Aroma Freedom Technique Session? _____

_____

_____

_____

_____

_____

_____

_____

_____

_____

_____

_____

_____

_____

_____

_____

_____

_____

_____

Program your mind daily! As soon as one affirmation is complete or the goal has been reached, create another. Make affirmations a daily habit and soon you will not feel right unless you have done your daily practice. This will keep you focused in the direction of your dreams. Feel free to experiment with different oils as you progress.

Date of Personal AFT Session: _____

Step 1 - Set Your Intention: _____
_____
_____

Rating your intention. How possible does it feel? (Circle One)

    Zero Hope - 0 1 2 3 4 5 6 7 8 9 10 - Absolute Confidence

Step 2 - What does the negative voice say that tells you this is not possible? _____
_____

Step 3 - How do you feel when you hear this negative voice (find ONE word)? _____
Step 4 - Where do you feel this in your body? _____
_____

Step 5 - Drift back to an earlier time when you felt the same way - get a snapshot or a movie. (Circle One)

    Snapshot   Movie   No Image

Notes on previous memory _____
_____
_____

Step 6 - Smell Memory Release Blend or other oils - specify which oils used: _____
Step 7 - Notice changes: _____
_____
_____

Step 8 - Is there a new belief or mindset that has emerged? _____
_____
_____

Step 9 - Read the original intention and rate it again - how possible does it feel now? (circle one)

    Zero Hope - 0 1 2 3 4 5 6 7 8 9 10 - Absolute Confidence

(If 8 or higher (or if no negative voice), skip to Step 10 - the Affirmation. If less than 8, return to Step 2 on next page.)

How far have you shifted thus far?

Starting number: _____ New Number: _____

Step 2 - Re-read the intention and listen for what else the negative voice says about why it can't happen. _____

_____

Step 3 - How do you feel when you hear the negative voice? (find ONE word) _____

Step 4 - Where do you feel this in your body? _____

_____

_____

Step 5 - Drift back to an earlier time when you felt the same way - get a snapshot or a movie. (Circle One)

Snapshot   Movie   No Image

Notes on previous memory: _____

_____

_____

Step 6 - Smell Memory Release Blend or other oils - specify which oils used: _____

Step 7 - Notice changes _____

_____

_____

Step 8 - Is there a new belief or mindset that has emerged? _____

_____

_____

Step 9 - Read the original intention and rate it again - how possible does it feel now? (circle)

Zero Hope - 0 1 2 3 4 5 6 7 8 9 10 - Absolute Confidence

Look how far you've shifted!

Starting number: _____ Second Number: _____

Final Number: _____

(Move forward to Step 10 - the Affirmation - even if you're not yet at an 8 or higher. More shifting will occur during the next 3 steps.)

Step 10 - Affirmation: _____

_____

_____

_____

Step 11 - Stand in Power Pose: Repeat the affirmation for 2 minutes, twice daily, with conviction while standing in a power pose. Smell _Believe_™ or _Transformation_™ Oil Blend as you do this. (You may choose another transforming oil if you'd like, such as _Build Your Dream_™, _Magnify Your Purpose_™, etc)

Repeat for _at least three consecutive days,_ or until you create a new affirmation. Check off each box when complete.

Always make sure that your energy feels clear when you say the statement. If you experience inner resistance, use the AFT process to identify and release any negative thoughts, feelings, or memories that come up.

Date	AM	PM

Step 12 - Make Your Plan of Action: _____

_____

_____

_____

_____

_____

Follow-up - What has changed in your life because of THIS Aroma Freedom Technique Session? _____

_____

_____

_____

_____

_____

_____

_____

_____

_____

_____

_____

_____

_____

_____

_____

_____

_____

Program your mind daily! As soon as one affirmation is complete or the goal has been reached, create another. Make affirmations a daily habit and soon you will not feel right unless you have done your daily practice. This will keep you focused in the direction of your dreams. Feel free to experiment with different oils as you progress.

Date of Personal AFT Session: _____

Step 1 - Set Your Intention: _____

_____

Rating your intention. How possible does it feel? (Circle One)

      Zero Hope - 0 1 2 3 4 5 6 7 8 9 10 - Absolute Confidence

Step 2 - What does the negative voice say that tells you this is not possible? _____

_____

Step 3 - How do you feel when you hear this negative voice (find ONE word)? _____

Step 4 - Where do you feel this in your body? _____

_____

Step 5 - Drift back to an earlier time when you felt the same way - get a snapshot or a movie. (Circle One)

      Snapshot   Movie   No Image

Notes on previous memory _____

_____

Step 6 - Smell Memory Release Blend or other oils - specify which oils used: _____

Step 7 - Notice changes: _____

_____

Step 8 - Is there a new belief or mindset that has emerged? _____

_____

Step 9 - Read the original intention and rate it again - how possible does it feel now? (circle one)

      Zero Hope - 0 1 2 3 4 5 6 7 8 9 10 - Absolute Confidence

(If 8 or higher (or if no negative voice), skip to Step 10 - the Affirmation. If less than 8, return to Step 2 on next page.)

How far have you shifted thus far?

       Starting number: _____ New Number: _____

Step 2 - Re-read the intention and listen for what else the negative voice says about why it can't happen. _____

_____

Step 3 - How do you feel when you hear the negative voice? (find ONE word) _____

Step 4 - Where do you feel this in your body? _____

_____

Step 5 - Drift back to an earlier time when you felt the same way - get a snapshot or a movie. (Circle One)

       Snapshot   Movie   No Image

Notes on previous memory: _____

_____

Step 6 - Smell Memory Release Blend or other oils - specify which oils used: _____

Step 7 - Notice changes _____

_____

Step 8 - Is there a new belief or mindset that has emerged? _____

_____

Step 9 - Read the original intention and rate it again - how possible does it feel now? (circle)

     Zero Hope - 0 1 2 3 4 5 6 7 8 9 10 - Absolute Confidence

Look how far you've shifted!

       Starting number: _____ Second Number: _____
               Final Number: _____

(Move forward to Step 10 - the Affirmation - even if you're not yet at an 8 or higher. More shifting will occur during the next 3 steps.)

Step 10 - Affirmation: _____

_____
_____
_____

Step 11 - Stand in Power Pose: Repeat the affirmation for 2 minutes, twice daily, with conviction while standing in a power pose. Smell *Believe*™ or *Transformation*™ Oil Blend as you do this. (You may choose another transforming oil if you'd like, such as *Build Your Dream*™, *Magnify Your Purpose*™, etc)

Repeat for _at least three consecutive days_, or until you create a new affirmation. Check off each box when complete.

Always make sure that your energy feels clear when you say the statement. If you experience inner resistance, use the AFT process to identify and release any negative thoughts, feelings, or memories that come up.

Date	AM	PM

Step 12 - Make Your Plan of Action: _____

_____
_____
_____
_____
_____
_____

Follow-up - What has changed in your life because of THIS Aroma Freedom Technique Session? _____

_____

_____

_____

_____

_____

_____

_____

_____

_____

_____

_____

_____

_____

_____

_____

_____

_____

_____

Program your mind daily! As soon as one affirmation is complete or the goal has been reached, create another. Make affirmations a daily habit and soon you will not feel right unless you have done your daily practice. This will keep you focused in the direction of your dreams. Feel free to experiment with different oils as you progress.

Date of Personal AFT Session: _____

Step 1 - Set Your Intention: _____
_____
_____

Rating your intention. How possible does it feel? (Circle One)

    Zero Hope - 0 1 2 3 4 5 6 7 8 9 10 - Absolute Confidence

Step 2 - What does the negative voice say that tells you this is not possible? _____
_____

Step 3 - How do you feel when you hear this negative voice (find ONE word)? _____

Step 4 - Where do you feel this in your body? _____

Step 5 - Drift back to an earlier time when you felt the same way - get a snapshot or a movie. (Circle One)

    Snapshot   Movie   No Image

Notes on previous memory _____
_____
_____

Step 6 - Smell Memory Release Blend or other oils - specify which oils used: _____

Step 7 - Notice changes: _____
_____
_____

Step 8 - Is there a new belief or mindset that has emerged? _____
_____
_____

Step 9 - Read the original intention and rate it again - how possible does it feel now? (circle one)

    Zero Hope - 0 1 2 3 4 5 6 7 8 9 10 - Absolute Confidence

(If 8 or higher (or if no negative voice), skip to Step 10 - the Affirmation. If less than 8, return to Step 2 on next page.)

How far have you shifted thus far?

Starting number: _____ New Number: _____

Step 2 - Re-read the intention and listen for what else the negative voice says about why it can't happen. _____

_____

Step 3 - How do you feel when you hear the negative voice? (find ONE word) _____

Step 4 - Where do you feel this in your body? _____

_____

Step 5 - Drift back to an earlier time when you felt the same way - get a snapshot or a movie. (Circle One)

Snapshot   Movie   No Image

Notes on previous memory: _____

_____

Step 6 - Smell Memory Release Blend or other oils - specify which oils used: _____

Step 7 - Notice changes _____

_____

Step 8 - Is there a new belief or mindset that has emerged? _____

_____

Step 9 - Read the original intention and rate it again - how possible does it feel now? (circle)

Zero Hope - 0 1 2 3 4 5 6 7 8 9 10 - Absolute Confidence

Look how far you've shifted!

Starting number: _____ Second Number: _____

Final Number: _____

(Move forward to Step 10 - the Affirmation - even if you're not yet at an 8 or higher. More shifting will occur during the next 3 steps.)

Step 10 - Affirmation: _____

_____

_____

_____

Step 11 - Stand in Power Pose: Repeat the affirmation for 2 minutes, twice daily, with conviction while standing in a power pose. Smell *Believe*™ or *Transformation*™ Oil Blend as you do this. (You may choose another transforming oil if you'd like, such as *Build Your Dream*™, *Magnify Your Purpose*™, etc)

Repeat for *at least three consecutive days,* or until you create a new affirmation. Check off each box when complete.

Always make sure that your energy feels clear when you say the statement. If you experience inner resistance, use the AFT process to identify and release any negative thoughts, feelings, or memories that come up.

Date	AM	PM

Step 12 - Make Your Plan of Action: _____

_____

_____

_____

_____

_____

Follow-up - What has changed in your life because of THIS Aroma Freedom Technique Session? _____

_____

_____

_____

_____

_____

_____

_____

_____

_____

_____

_____

_____

_____

_____

_____

_____

_____

_____

_____

Program your mind daily! As soon as one affirmation is complete or the goal has been reached, create another. Make affirmations a daily habit and soon you will not feel right unless you have done your daily practice. This will keep you focused in the direction of your dreams. Feel free to experiment with different oils as you progress.

Date of Personal AFT Session: _____

Step 1 - Set Your Intention: _____
_____

Rating your intention. How possible does it feel? (Circle One)

Zero Hope - 0 1 2 3 4 5 6 7 8 9 10 - Absolute Confidence

Step 2 - What does the negative voice say that tells you this is not possible? _____

Step 3 - How do you feel when you hear this negative voice (find ONE word)? _____

Step 4 - Where do you feel this in your body? _____

Step 5 - Drift back to an earlier time when you felt the same way - get a snapshot or a movie. (Circle One)

Snapshot   Movie   No Image

Notes on previous memory _____
_____

Step 6 - Smell Memory Release Blend or other oils - specify which oils used: _____

Step 7 - Notice changes: _____
_____

Step 8 - Is there a new belief or mindset that has emerged? _____
_____

Step 9 - Read the original intention and rate it again - how possible does it feel now? (circle one)

Zero Hope - 0 1 2 3 4 5 6 7 8 9 10 - Absolute Confidence

(If 8 or higher (or if no negative voice), skip to Step 10 - the Affirmation. If less than 8, return to Step 2 on next page.)

45

How far have you shifted thus far?

Starting number: _____ New Number: _____

Step 2 - Re-read the intention and listen for what else the negative voice says about why it can't happen. _____

_____

Step 3 - How do you feel when you hear the negative voice? (find ONE word) _____

Step 4 - Where do you feel this in your body? _____

_____

Step 5 - Drift back to an earlier time when you felt the same way - get a snapshot or a movie. (Circle One)

Snapshot   Movie   No Image

Notes on previous memory: _____

_____

Step 6 - Smell Memory Release Blend or other oils - specify which oils used: _____

Step 7 - Notice changes _____

_____

Step 8 - Is there a new belief or mindset that has emerged? _____

_____

Step 9 - Read the original intention and rate it again - how possible does it feel now? (circle)

Zero Hope - 0 1 2 3 4 5 6 7 8 9 10 - Absolute Confidence

Look how far you've shifted!

Starting number: _____ Second Number: _____

Final Number: _____

(Move forward to Step 10 - the Affirmation - even if you're not yet at an 8 or higher. More shifting will occur during the next 3 steps.)

Step 10 - Affirmation: _____

_____

_____

_____

Step 11 - Stand in Power Pose: Repeat the affirmation for 2 minutes, twice daily, with conviction while standing in a power pose. Smell *Relieve*™ or *Transformation*™ Oil Blend as you do this. (You may choose another transforming oil if you'd like, such as *Build Your Dream*™, *Magnify Your Purpose*™, etc)

Repeat for _at least three consecutive days_, or until you create a new affirmation. Check off each box when complete.

Always make sure that your energy feels clear when you say the statement. If you experience inner resistance, use the AFT process to identify and release any negative thoughts, feelings, or memories that come up.

Date	AM	PM

Step 12 - Make Your Plan of Action: _____

_____

_____

_____

_____

_____

Follow-up - What has changed in your life because of THIS Aroma Freedom Technique Session? _____

_____

_____

_____

_____

_____

_____

_____

_____

_____

_____

_____

_____

_____

_____

_____

_____

_____

_____

Program your mind daily! As soon as one affirmation is complete or the goal has been reached, create another. Make affirmations a daily habit and soon you will not feel right unless you have done your daily practice. This will keep you focused in the direction of your dreams. Feel free to experiment with different oils as you progress.

Date of Personal AFT Session: _____

Step 1 - Set Your Intention: _____
_____
_____

Rating your intention. How possible does it feel? (Circle One)

    Zero Hope - 0 1 2 3 4 5 6 7 8 9 10 - Absolute Confidence

Step 2 - What does the negative voice say that tells you this is not possible? _____
_____

Step 3 - How do you feel when you hear this negative voice (find ONE word)? _____
Step 4 - Where do you feel this in your body? _____

Step 5 - Drift back to an earlier time when you felt the same way - get a snapshot or a movie. (Circle One)

       Snapshot   Movie   No Image

Notes on previous memory _____
_____

Step 6 - Smell Memory Release Blend or other oils - specify which oils used: _____
Step 7 - Notice changes: _____
_____

Step 8 - Is there a new belief or mindset that has emerged? _____
_____

Step 9 - Read the original intention and rate it again - how possible does it feel now? (circle one)

    Zero Hope - 0 1 2 3 4 5 6 7 8 9 10 - Absolute Confidence

(If 8 or higher (or if no negative voice), skip to Step 10 - the Affirmation. If less than 8, return to Step 2 on next page.)

How far have you shifted thus far?

Starting number: _____ New Number: _____

Step 2 - Re-read the intention and listen for what else the negative voice says about why it can't happen. _____

_____

Step 3 - How do you feel when you hear the negative voice? (find ONE word) _____

Step 4 - Where do you feel this in your body? _____

_____

Step 5 - Drift back to an earlier time when you felt the same way - get a snapshot or a movie. (Circle One)

Snapshot   Movie   No Image

Notes on previous memory: _____

_____

Step 6 - Smell Memory Release Blend or other oils - specify which oils used: _____

Step 7 - Notice changes _____

_____

Step 8 - Is there a new belief or mindset that has emerged? _____

_____

Step 9 - Read the original intention and rate it again - how possible does it feel now? (circle)

Zero Hope - 0 1 2 3 4 5 6 7 8 9 10 - Absolute Confidence

Look how far you've shifted!

Starting number: _____ Second Number: _____

Final Number: _____

(Move forward to Step 10 - the Affirmation - even if you're not yet at an 8 or higher. More shifting will occur during the next 3 steps.)

Step 10 - Affirmation: _____

_____

_____

_____

Step 11 - Stand in Power Pose: Repeat the affirmation for 2 minutes, twice daily, with conviction while standing in a power pose. Smell _Believe_™ or _Transformation_™ Oil Blend as you do this. (You may choose another transforming oil if you'd like, such as _Build Your Dream_™, _Magnify Your Purpose_™, etc)

Repeat for _at least three consecutive days,_ or until you create a new affirmation. Check off each box when complete.

Always make sure that your energy feels clear when you say the statement. If you experience inner resistance, use the AFT process to identify and release any negative thoughts, feelings, or memories that come up.

Date	AM	PM

Step 12 - Make Your Plan of Action: _____

_____

_____

_____

_____

_____

_____

Follow-up - What has changed in your life because of THIS Aroma Freedom Technique Session? _____

_____
_____
_____
_____
_____
_____
_____
_____
_____
_____
_____
_____
_____
_____
_____
_____
_____
_____
_____

Program your mind daily! As soon as one affirmation is complete or the goal has been reached, create another. Make affirmations a daily habit and soon you will not feel right unless you have done your daily practice. This will keep you focused in the direction of your dreams. Feel free to experiment with different oils as you progress.

Date of Personal AFT Session: _____

Step 1 - Set Your Intention: _____

_____

Rating your intention. How possible does it feel? (Circle One)

    Zero Hope - 0 1 2 3 4 5 6 7 8 9 10 - Absolute Confidence

Step 2 - What does the negative voice say that tells you this is not possible? _____

Step 3 - How do you feel when you hear this negative voice (find ONE word)? _____

Step 4 - Where do you feel this in your body? _____

Step 5 - Drift back to an earlier time when you felt the same way - get a snapshot or a movie. (Circle One)

    Snapshot   Movie   No Image

Notes on previous memory _____

_____

Step 6 - Smell Memory Release Blend or other oils - specify which oils used: _____

Step 7 - Notice changes: _____

_____

Step 8 - Is there a new belief or mindset that has emerged? _____

_____

Step 9 - Read the original intention and rate it again - how possible does it feel now? (circle one)

    Zero Hope - 0 1 2 3 4 5 6 7 8 9 10 - Absolute Confidence

(If 8 or higher (or if no negative voice), skip to Step 10 - the Affirmation. If less than 8, return to Step 2 on next page.)

How far have you shifted thus far?

Starting number: _____ New Number: _____

Step 2 - Re-read the intention and listen for what else the negative voice says about why it can't happen. _____

_____

Step 3 - How do you feel when you hear the negative voice? (find ONE word) _____

Step 4 - Where do you feel this in your body? _____

_____

Step 5 - Drift back to an earlier time when you felt the same way - get a snapshot or a movie. (Circle One)

Snapshot   Movie   No Image

Notes on previous memory: _____

_____

Step 6 - Smell Memory Release Blend or other oils - specify which oils used: _____

Step 7 - Notice changes _____

_____

Step 8 - Is there a new belief or mindset that has emerged? _____

_____

Step 9 - Read the original intention and rate it again - how possible does it feel now? (circle)

Zero Hope - 0 1 2 3 4 5 6 7 8 9 10 - Absolute Confidence

Look how far you've shifted!

Starting number: _____ Second Number: _____

Final Number: _____

(Move forward to Step 10 - the Affirmation - even if you're not yet at an 8 or higher. More shifting will occur during the next 3 steps.)

Step 10 - Affirmation: _____

_____
_____
_____

Step 11 - Stand in Power Pose: Repeat the affirmation for 2 minutes, twice daily, with conviction while standing in a power pose. Smell *Believe*™ or *Transformation*™ Oil Blend as you do this. (You may choose another transforming oil if you'd like, such as *Build Your Dream*™, *Magnify Your Purpose*™, etc)

Repeat for *at least three consecutive days,* or until you create a new affirmation. Check off each box when complete.

Always make sure that your energy feels clear when you say the statement. If you experience inner resistance, use the AFT process to identify and release any negative thoughts, feelings, or memories that come up.

Date	AM	PM

Step 12 - Make Your Plan of Action: _____

_____
_____
_____
_____
_____

Follow-up - What has changed in your life because of THIS Aroma Freedom Technique Session? _____

_____

_____

_____

_____

_____

_____

_____

_____

_____

_____

_____

_____

_____

_____

_____

_____

_____

_____

Program your mind daily! As soon as one affirmation is complete or the goal has been reached, create another. Make affirmations a daily habit and soon you will not feel right unless you have done your daily practice. This will keep you focused in the direction of your dreams. Feel free to experiment with different oils as you progress.

Date of Personal AFT Session: _____

Step 1 - Set Your Intention: _____
_____

Rating your intention. How possible does it feel? (Circle One)

    Zero Hope   0 1 2 3 4 5 6 7 8 9 10 - Absolute Confidence

Step 2 - What does the negative voice say that tells you this is not possible? _____

Step 3 - How do you feel when you hear this negative voice (find ONE word)? _____

Step 4 - Where do you feel this in your body? _____

Step 5 - Drift back to an earlier time when you felt the same way - get a snapshot or a movie. (Circle One)

       Snapshot   Movie   No Image

Notes on previous memory _____
_____

Step 6 - Smell Memory Release Blend or other oils - specify which oils used: _____

Step 7 - Notice changes: _____
_____

Step 8 - Is there a new belief or mindset that has emerged? _____
_____

Step 9 - Read the original intention and rate it again - how possible does it feel now? (circle one)

    Zero Hope - 0 1 2 3 4 5 6 7 8 9 10 - Absolute Confidence

(If 8 or higher (or if no negative voice), skip to Step 10 - the Affirmation. If less than 8, return to Step 2 on next page.)

How far have you shifted thus far?

Starting number: _____ New Number: _____

Step 2 - Re-read the intention and listen for what else the negative voice says about why it can't happen. _____

_____

Step 3 - How do you feel when you hear the negative voice? (find ONE word) _____

Step 4 - Where do you feel this in your body? _____

_____

_____

Step 5 - Drift back to an earlier time when you felt the same way - get a snapshot or a movie. (Circle One)

Snapshot   Movie   No Image

Notes on previous memory: _____

_____

_____

Step 6 - Smell Memory Release Blend or other oils - specify which oils used: _____

Step 7 - Notice changes _____

_____

_____

Step 8 - Is there a new belief or mindset that has emerged? _____

_____

_____

Step 9 - Read the original intention and rate it again - how possible does it feel now? (circle)

Zero Hope - 0 1 2 3 4 5 6 7 8 9 10 - Absolute Confidence

Look how far you've shifted!

Starting number: _____ Second Number: _____

Final Number: _____

(Move forward to Step 10 - the Affirmation - even if you're not yet at an 8 or higher. More shifting will occur during the next 3 steps.)

Step 10 - Affirmation: _____

_____

_____

_____

Step 11 - Stand in Power Pose: Repeat the affirmation for 2 minutes, twice daily, with conviction while standing in a power pose. Smell *Believe*™ or *Transformation*™ Oil Blend as you do this. (You may choose another transforming oil if you'd like, such as *Build Your Dream*™, *Magnify Your Purpose*™, etc)

Repeat for _at least three consecutive days,_ or until you create a new affirmation. Check off each box when complete.

Always make sure that your energy feels clear when you say the statement. If you experience inner resistance, use the AFT process to identify and release any negative thoughts, feelings, or memories that come up.

Date	AM	PM

Step 12 - Make Your Plan of Action: _____

_____

_____

_____

_____

_____

Follow-up - What has changed in your life because of THIS Aroma Freedom Technique Session? _____

_____

_____

_____

_____

_____

_____

_____

_____

_____

_____

_____

_____

_____

_____

_____

_____

_____

_____

_____

_____

Program your mind daily! As soon as one affirmation is complete or the goal has been reached, create another. Make affirmations a daily habit and soon you will not feel right unless you have done your daily practice. This will keep you focused in the direction of your dreams. Feel free to experiment with different oils as you progress.

Date of Personal AFT Session: _____

Step 1 - Set Your Intention: _____
_____

Rating your intention. How possible does it feel? (Circle One)

    Zero Hope - 0 1 2 3 4 5 6 7 8 9 10 - Absolute Confidence

Step 2 - What does the negative voice say that tells you this is not possible? _____

Step 3 - How do you feel when you hear this negative voice (find ONE word)? _____

Step 4 - Where do you feel this in your body? _____

Step 5 - Drift back to an earlier time when you felt the same way - get a snapshot or a movie. (Circle One)

    Snapshot   Movie   No Image

Notes on previous memory _____
_____

Step 6 - Smell Memory Release Blend or other oils - specify which oils used: _____

Step 7 - Notice changes: _____
_____

Step 8 - Is there a new belief or mindset that has emerged? _____
_____

Step 9 - Read the original intention and rate it again - how possible does it feel now? (circle one)

    Zero Hope - 0 1 2 3 4 5 6 7 8 9 10 - Absolute Confidence

(If 8 or higher (or if no negative voice), skip to Step 10 - the Affirmation. If less than 8, return to Step 2 on next page.)

How far have you shifted thus far?

       Starting number: _____ New Number: _____

Step 2 - Re-read the intention and listen for what else the negative voice says about why it can't happen. _____

_____

Step 3 - How do you feel when you hear the negative voice? (find ONE word) _____

Step 4 - Where do you feel this in your body? _____

_____

Step 5 - Drift back to an earlier time when you felt the same way - get a snapshot or a movie. (Circle One)

      Snapshot   Movie   No Image

Notes on previous memory: _____

_____

Step 6 - Smell Memory Release Blend or other oils - specify which oils used: _____

Step 7 - Notice changes _____

_____

Step 8 - Is there a new belief or mindset that has emerged? _____

_____

Step 9 - Read the original intention and rate it again - how possible does it feel now? (circle)

     Zero Hope - 0 1 2 3 4 5 6 7 8 9 10 - Absolute Confidence

Look how far you've shifted!

       Starting number: _____ Second Number: _____

            Final Number: _____

(Move forward to Step 10 - the Affirmation - even if you're not yet at an 8 or higher. More shifting will occur during the next 3 steps.)

Step 10 - Affirmation: _____

_____

_____

_____

Step 11 - Stand in Power Pose: Repeat the affirmation for 2 minutes, twice daily, with conviction while standing in a power pose. Smell *Believe*™ or *Transformation*™ Oil Blend as you do this. (You may choose another transforming oil if you'd like, such as *Build Your Dream*™, *Magnify Your Purpose*™, etc)

Repeat for <u>at least three consecutive days</u>, or until you create a new affirmation. Check off each box when complete.

Always make sure that your energy feels clear when you say the statement. If you experience inner resistance, use the AFT process to identify and release any negative thoughts, feelings, or memories that come up.

Date	AM	PM

Step 12 - Make Your Plan of Action: _____

_____

_____

_____

_____

_____

Follow-up - What has changed in your life because of THIS Aroma Freedom Technique Session? _____

_____

_____

_____

_____

_____

_____

_____

_____

_____

_____

_____

_____

_____

_____

_____

_____

_____

_____

_____

Program your mind daily! As soon as one affirmation is complete or the goal has been reached, create another. Make affirmations a daily habit and soon you will not feel right unless you have done your daily practice. This will keep you focused in the direction of your dreams. Feel free to experiment with different oils as you progress.

Date of Personal AFT Session: _____

Step 1 - Set Your Intention: _____
_____

Rating your intention. How possible does it feel? (Circle One)

    Zero Hope - 0 1 2 3 4 5 6 7 8 9 10 - Absolute Confidence

Step 2 - What does the negative voice say that tells you this is not possible? _____

Step 3 - How do you feel when you hear this negative voice (find ONE word)? _____

Step 4 - Where do you feel this in your body? _____

Step 5 - Drift back to an earlier time when you felt the same way - get a snapshot or a movie. (Circle One)

    Snapshot   Movie   No Image

Notes on previous memory _____
_____

Step 6 - Smell Memory Release Blend or other oils - specify which oils used: _____

Step 7 - Notice changes: _____
_____

Step 8 - Is there a new belief or mindset that has emerged? _____
_____

Step 9 - Read the original intention and rate it again - how possible does it feel now? (circle one)

    Zero Hope - 0 1 2 3 4 5 6 7 8 9 10 - Absolute Confidence

(If 8 or higher (or if no negative voice), skip to Step 10 - the Affirmation. If less than 8, return to Step 2 on next page.)

How far have you shifted thus far?

Starting number: _____ New Number: _____

Step 2 - Re-read the intention and listen for what else the negative voice says about why it can't happen. _____

_____

Step 3 - How do you feel when you hear the negative voice? (find ONE word) _____

Step 4 - Where do you feel this in your body? _____

_____

Step 5 - Drift back to an earlier time when you felt the same way - get a snapshot or a movie. (Circle One)

Snapshot   Movie   No Image

Notes on previous memory: _____

_____

Step 6 - Smell Memory Release Blend or other oils - specify which oils used: _____

Step 7 - Notice changes _____

_____

Step 8 - Is there a new belief or mindset that has emerged? _____

_____

Step 9 - Read the original intention and rate it again - how possible does it feel now? (circle)

Zero Hope - 0 1 2 3 4 5 6 7 8 9 10 - Absolute Confidence

Look how far you've shifted!

Starting number: _____ Second Number: _____

Final Number: _____

(Move forward to Step 10 - the Affirmation - even if you're not yet at an 8 or higher. More shifting will occur during the next 3 steps.)

Step 10 - Affirmation: _____

_____
_____
_____

Step 11 - Stand in Power Pose: Repeat the affirmation for 2 minutes, twice daily, with conviction while standing in a power pose. Smell *Relieve*™ or *Transformation*™ Oil Blend as you do this. (You may choose another transforming oil if you'd like, such as *Build Your Dream*™, *Magnify Your Purpose*™, etc)

Repeat for *at least three consecutive days*, or until you create a new affirmation. Check off each box when complete.

Always make sure that your energy feels clear when you say the statement. If you experience inner resistance, use the AFT process to identify and release any negative thoughts, feelings, or memories that come up.

Date	AM	PM

Step 12 - Make Your Plan of Action: _____

_____
_____
_____
_____
_____

Follow-up - What has changed in your life because of THIS Aroma Freedom Technique Session? _____

_____
_____
_____
_____
_____
_____
_____
_____
_____
_____
_____
_____
_____
_____
_____
_____
_____
_____
_____

Program your mind daily! As soon as one affirmation is complete or the goal has been reached, create another. Make affirmations a daily habit and soon you will not feel right unless you have done your daily practice. This will keep you focused in the direction of your dreams. Feel free to experiment with different oils as you progress.

Date of Personal AFT Session: _____

Step 1 - Set Your Intention: _____
_____
_____

Rating your intention. How possible does it feel? (Circle One)

    Zero Hope - 0 1 2 3 4 5 6 7 8 9 10 - Absolute Confidence

Step 2 - What does the negative voice say that tells you this is not possible? _____
_____

Step 3 - How do you feel when you hear this negative voice (find ONE word)? _____
Step 4 - Where do you feel this in your body? _____

Step 5 - Drift back to an earlier time when you felt the same way - get a snapshot or a movie. (Circle One)

    Snapshot   Movie   No Image

Notes on previous memory _____
_____
_____

Step 6 - Smell Memory Release Blend or other oils - specify which oils used: _____
Step 7 - Notice changes: _____
_____
_____

Step 8 - Is there a new belief or mindset that has emerged? _____
_____
_____

Step 9 - Read the original intention and rate it again - how possible does it feel now? (circle one)

    Zero Hope - 0 1 2 3 4 5 6 7 8 9 10 - Absolute Confidence

(If 8 or higher (or if no negative voice), skip to Step 10 - the Affirmation. If less than 8, return to Step 2 on next page.)

69

How far have you shifted thus far?

Starting number: _____ New Number: _____

Step 2 - Re-read the intention and listen for what else the negative voice says about why it can't happen. _____

_____

Step 3 - How do you feel when you hear the negative voice? (find ONE word) _____

Step 4 - Where do you feel this in your body? _____

_____

Step 5 - Drift back to an earlier time when you felt the same way - get a snapshot or a movie. (Circle One)

Snapshot   Movie   No Image

Notes on previous memory: _____

_____

Step 6 - Smell Memory Release Blend or other oils - specify which oils used: _____

Step 7 - Notice changes _____

_____

Step 8 - Is there a new belief or mindset that has emerged? _____

_____

Step 9 - Read the original intention and rate it again - how possible does it feel now? (circle)

Zero Hope - 0 1 2 3 4 5 6 7 8 9 10 - Absolute Confidence

Look how far you've shifted!

Starting number: _____ Second Number: _____

Final Number: _____

(Move forward to Step 10 - the Affirmation - even if you're not yet at an 8 or higher. More shifting will occur during the next 3 steps.)

Step 10 - Affirmation: _____

_____

_____

_____

Step 11 - Stand in Power Pose: Repeat the affirmation for 2 minutes, twice daily, with conviction while standing in a power pose. Smell *Relieve*™ or *Transformation*™ Oil Blend as you do this. (You may choose another transforming oil if you'd like, such as *Build Your Dream*™, *Magnify Your Purpose*™, etc)

Repeat for *at least three consecutive days,* or until you create a new affirmation. Check off each box when complete.

Always make sure that your energy feels clear when you say the statement. If you experience inner resistance, use the AFT process to identify and release any negative thoughts, feelings, or memories that come up.

Date	AM	PM

Step 12 - Make Your Plan of Action: _____

_____

_____

_____

_____

_____

_____

Follow-up - What has changed in your life because of THIS Aroma Freedom Technique Session? _____

_____

_____

_____

_____

_____

_____

_____

_____

_____

_____

_____

_____

_____

_____

_____

_____

_____

_____

Program your mind daily! As soon as one affirmation is complete or the goal has been reached, create another. Make affirmations a daily habit and soon you will not feel right unless you have done your daily practice. This will keep you focused in the direction of your dreams. Feel free to experiment with different oils as you progress.

Date of Personal AFT Session: _____

Step 1 - Set Your Intention: _____
_____

Rating your intention. How possible does it feel? (Circle One)

   Zero Hope - 0 1 2 3 4 5 6 7 8 9 10 - Absolute Confidence

Step 2 - What does the negative voice say that tells you this is not possible? _____

Step 3 - How do you feel when you hear this negative voice (find ONE word)? _____

Step 4 - Where do you feel this in your body? _____

Step 5 - Drift back to an earlier time when you felt the same way - get a snapshot or a movie. (Circle One)

      Snapshot   Movie   No Image

Notes on previous memory _____
_____
_____

Step 6 - Smell Memory Release Blend or other oils - specify which oils used: _____

Step 7 - Notice changes: _____
_____
_____

Step 8 - Is there a new belief or mindset that has emerged? _____
_____
_____

Step 9 - Read the original intention and rate it again - how possible does it feel now? (circle one)

   Zero Hope - 0 1 2 3 4 5 6 7 8 9 10 - Absolute Confidence

(If 8 or higher (or if no negative voice), skip to Step 10 - the Affirmation. If less than 8, return to Step 2 on next page.)

How far have you shifted thus far?

Starting number: _____ New Number: _____

Step 2 - Re-read the intention and listen for what else the negative voice says about why it can't happen. _____

_____

Step 3 - How do you feel when you hear the negative voice? (find ONE word) _____

Step 4 - Where do you feel this in your body? _____

_____

Step 5 - Drift back to an earlier time when you felt the same way - get a snapshot or a movie. (Circle One)

Snapshot   Movie   No Image

Notes on previous memory: _____

_____

Step 6 - Smell Memory Release Blend or other oils - specify which oils used: _____

Step 7 - Notice changes _____

_____

Step 8 - Is there a new belief or mindset that has emerged? _____

_____

Step 9 - Read the original intention and rate it again - how possible does it feel now? (circle)

Zero Hope - 0 1 2 3 4 5 6 7 8 9 10 - Absolute Confidence

Look how far you've shifted!

Starting number: _____ Second Number: _____

Final Number: _____

(Move forward to Step 10 - the Affirmation - even if you're not yet at an 8 or higher. More shifting will occur during the next 3 steps.)

Step 10 - Affirmation: _____

_____

_____

_____

Step 11 - Stand in Power Pose: Repeat the affirmation for 2 minutes, twice daily, with conviction while standing in a power pose. Smell _Believe_™ or _Transformation_™ Oil Blend as you do this. (You may choose another transforming oil if you'd like, such as _Build Your Dream_™, _Magnify Your Purpose_™, etc)

Repeat for _at least three consecutive days_, or until you create a new affirmation. Check off each box when complete.

Always make sure that your energy feels clear when you say the statement. If you experience inner resistance, use the AFT process to identify and release any negative thoughts, feelings, or memories that come up.

Date	AM	PM

Step 12 - Make Your Plan of Action: _____

_____

_____

_____

_____

_____

_____

Follow-up - What has changed in your life because of THIS Aroma Freedom Technique Session? _____

_____

_____

_____

_____

_____

_____

_____

_____

_____

_____

_____

_____

_____

_____

_____

_____

_____

_____

Program your mind daily! As soon as one affirmation is complete or the goal has been reached, create another. Make affirmations a daily habit and soon you will not feel right unless you have done your daily practice. This will keep you focused in the direction of your dreams. Feel free to experiment with different oils as you progress.

Date of Personal AFT Session: _____

Step 1 - Set Your Intention: _____
_____
_____

Rating your intention. How possible does it feel? (Circle One)

    Zero Hope   0 1 2 3 4 5 6 7 8 9 10 - Absolute Confidence

Step 2 - What does the negative voice say that tells you this is not possible? _____
_____

Step 3 - How do you feel when you hear this negative voice (find ONE word)? _____

Step 4 - Where do you feel this in your body? _____

Step 5 - Drift back to an earlier time when you felt the same way - get a snapshot or a movie. (Circle One)

    Snapshot   Movie   No Image

Notes on previous memory _____
_____
_____

Step 6 - Smell Memory Release Blend or other oils - specify which oils used: _____

Step 7 - Notice changes: _____
_____
_____

Step 8 - Is there a new belief or mindset that has emerged? _____
_____
_____

Step 9 - Read the original intention and rate it again - how possible does it feel now? (circle one)

    Zero Hope - 0 1 2 3 4 5 6 7 8 9 10 - Absolute Confidence

(If 8 or higher (or if no negative voice), skip to Step 10 - the Affirmation. If less than 8, return to Step 2 on next page.)

How far have you shifted thus far?

Starting number: _____ New Number: _____

Step 2 - Re-read the intention and listen for what else the negative voice says about why it can't happen. _____

_____

Step 3 - How do you feel when you hear the negative voice? (find ONE word) _____

Step 4 - Where do you feel this in your body? _____

_____

Step 5 - Drift back to an earlier time when you felt the same way - get a snapshot or a movie. (Circle One)

Snapshot　　　Movie　　　No Image

Notes on previous memory: _____

_____

Step 6 - Smell Memory Release Blend or other oils - specify which oils used: _____

Step 7 - Notice changes _____

_____

Step 8 - Is there a new belief or mindset that has emerged? _____

_____

Step 9 - Read the original intention and rate it again - how possible does it feel now? (circle)

Zero Hope - 0 1 2 3 4 5 6 7 8 9 10 - Absolute Confidence

Look how far you've shifted!

Starting number: _____ Second Number: _____

Final Number: _____

(Move forward to Step 10 - the Affirmation - even if you're not yet at an 8 or higher. More shifting will occur during the next 3 steps.)

Step 10 - Affirmation: _____

_____

_____

_____

Step 11 - Stand in Power Pose: Repeat the affirmation for 2 minutes, twice daily, with conviction while standing in a power pose. Smell _Believe_™ or _Transformation_™ Oil Blend as you do this. (You may choose another transforming oil if you'd like, such as _Build Your Dream_™, _Magnify Your Purpose_™, etc)

Repeat for _at least three consecutive days,_ or until you create a new affirmation. Check off each box when complete.

Always make sure that your energy feels clear when you say the statement. If you experience inner resistance, use the AFT process to identify and release any negative thoughts, feelings, or memories that come up.

Date	AM	PM

Step 12 - Make Your Plan of Action: _____

_____

_____

_____

_____

_____

_____

Follow-up - What has changed in your life because of THIS Aroma Freedom Technique Session? _____

_____

_____

_____

_____

_____

_____

_____

_____

_____

_____

_____

_____

_____

_____

_____

_____

_____

_____

_____

Program your mind daily! As soon as one affirmation is complete or the goal has been reached, create another. Make affirmations a daily habit and soon you will not feel right unless you have done your daily practice. This will keep you focused in the direction of your dreams. Feel free to experiment with different oils as you progress.

Date of Personal AFT Session: _____

Step 1 - Set Your Intention: _____
_____

Rating your intention. How possible does it feel? (Circle One)

    Zero Hope - 0　1　2　3　4　5　6　7　8　9　10 - Absolute Confidence

Step 2 - What does the negative voice say that tells you this is not possible? _____

Step 3 - How do you feel when you hear this negative voice (find ONE word)? _____

Step 4 - Where do you feel this in your body? _____

Step 5 - Drift back to an earlier time when you felt the same way - get a snapshot or a movie. (Circle One)

      Snapshot　　　Movie　　　No Image

Notes on previous memory _____
_____

Step 6 - Smell Memory Release Blend or other oils - specify which oils used: _____

Step 7 - Notice changes: _____
_____

Step 8 - Is there a new belief or mindset that has emerged? _____
_____

Step 9 - Read the original intention and rate it again - how possible does it feel now? (circle one)

    Zero Hope - 0　1　2　3　4　5　6　7　8　9　10 - Absolute Confidence

(If 8 or higher (or if no negative voice), skip to Step 10 - the Affirmation. If less than 8, return to Step 2 on next page.)

81

How far have you shifted thus far?

Starting number: _____ New Number: _____

Step 2 - Re-read the intention and listen for what else the negative voice says about why it can't happen. _____

_____

Step 3 - How do you feel when you hear the negative voice? (find ONE word) _____

Step 4 - Where do you feel this in your body? _____

_____

Step 5 - Drift back to an earlier time when you felt the same way - get a snapshot or a movie. (Circle One)

Snapshot   Movie   No Image

Notes on previous memory: _____

_____

Step 6 - Smell Memory Release Blend or other oils - specify which oils used: _____

Step 7 - Notice changes _____

_____

Step 8 - Is there a new belief or mindset that has emerged? _____

_____

Step 9 - Read the original intention and rate it again - how possible does it feel now? (circle)

Zero Hope - 0 1 2 3 4 5 6 7 8 9 10 - Absolute Confidence

Look how far you've shifted!

Starting number: _____ Second Number: _____

Final Number: _____

(Move forward to Step 10 - the Affirmation - even if you're not yet at an 8 or higher. More shifting will occur during the next 3 steps.)

Step 10 - Affirmation: _____

_____

_____

_____

Step 11 - Stand in Power Pose: Repeat the affirmation for 2 minutes, twice daily, with conviction while standing in a power pose. Smell *Believe*™ or *Transformation*™ Oil Blend as you do this. (You may choose another transforming oil if you'd like, such as *Build Your Dream*™, *Magnify Your Purpose*™, etc)

Repeat for <u>*at least three consecutive days*</u>, or until you create a new affirmation. Check off each box when complete.

Always make sure that your energy feels clear when you say the statement. If you experience inner resistance, use the AFT process to identify and release any negative thoughts, feelings, or memories that come up.

Date	AM	PM

Step 12 - Make Your Plan of Action: _____

_____

_____

_____

_____

Follow-up - What has changed in your life because of THIS Aroma Freedom Technique Session? _____

_____

_____

_____

_____

_____

_____

_____

_____

_____

_____

_____

_____

_____

_____

_____

_____

_____

_____

Program your mind daily! As soon as one affirmation is complete or the goal has been reached, create another. Make affirmations a daily habit and soon you will not feel right unless you have done your daily practice. This will keep you focused in the direction of your dreams. Feel free to experiment with different oils as you progress.

Date of Personal AFT Session: _____

Step 1 - Set Your Intention: _____
_____

Rating your intention. How possible does it feel? (Circle One)

      Zero Hope - 0 1 2 3 4 5 6 7 8 9 10 - Absolute Confidence

Step 2 - What does the negative voice say that tells you this is not possible? _____
_____

Step 3 - How do you feel when you hear this negative voice (find ONE word)? _____

Step 4 - Where do you feel this in your body? _____

Step 5 - Drift back to an earlier time when you felt the same way - get a snapshot or a movie. (Circle One)

      Snapshot   Movie   No Image

Notes on previous memory _____
_____

Step 6 - Smell Memory Release Blend or other oils - specify which oils used: _____

Step 7 - Notice changes: _____
_____

Step 8 - Is there a new belief or mindset that has emerged? _____
_____

Step 9 - Read the original intention and rate it again - how possible does it feel now? (circle one)

      Zero Hope - 0 1 2 3 4 5 6 7 8 9 10 - Absolute Confidence

(If 8 or higher (or if no negative voice), skip to Step 10 - the Affirmation. If less than 8, return to Step 2 on next page.)

85

How far have you shifted thus far?

       Starting number: _____ New Number: _____

Step 2 - Re-read the intention and listen for what else the negative voice says about why it can't happen. _____

_____

Step 3 - How do you feel when you hear the negative voice? (find ONE word) _____

Step 4 - Where do you feel this in your body? _____

_____

Step 5 - Drift back to an earlier time when you felt the same way - get a snapshot or a movie. (Circle One)

      Snapshot   Movie   No Image

Notes on previous memory: _____

_____

Step 6 - Smell Memory Release Blend or other oils - specify which oils used: _____

Step 7 - Notice changes _____

_____

Step 8 - Is there a new belief or mindset that has emerged? _____

_____

Step 9 - Read the original intention and rate it again - how possible does it feel now? (circle)

     Zero Hope - 0 1 2 3 4 5 6 7 8 9 10 - Absolute Confidence

Look how far you've shifted!

      Starting number: _____ Second Number: _____

           Final Number: _____

(Move forward to Step 10 - the Affirmation - even if you're not yet at an 8 or higher. More shifting will occur during the next 3 steps.)

Step 10 - Affirmation: _____

_____

_____
_____
_____

Step 11 - Stand in Power Pose: Repeat the affirmation for 2 minutes, twice daily, with conviction while standing in a power pose. Smell *Believe™* or *Transformation™* Oil Blend as you do this. (You may choose another transforming oil if you'd like, such as *Build Your Dream™, Magnify Your Purpose™*, etc)

Repeat for *at least three consecutive days*, or until you create a new affirmation. Check off each box when complete.

Always make sure that your energy feels clear when you say the statement. If you experience inner resistance, use the AFT process to identify and release any negative thoughts, feelings, or memories that come up.

Date	AM	PM

Step 12 - Make Your Plan of Action: _____

_____
_____
_____
_____
_____
_____

Follow-up - What has changed in your life because of THIS Aroma Freedom Technique Session? _____

_____

_____

_____

_____

_____

_____

_____

_____

_____

_____

_____

_____

_____

_____

_____

_____

_____

_____

Program your mind daily! As soon as one affirmation is complete or the goal has been reached, create another. Make affirmations a daily habit and soon you will not feel right unless you have done your daily practice. This will keep you focused in the direction of your dreams. Feel free to experiment with different oils as you progress.

Date of Personal AFT Session: _____

Step 1 - Set Your Intention: _____
_____
_____

Rating your intention. How possible does it feel? (Circle One)

     Zero Hope - 0 1 2 3 4 5 6 7 8 9 10 - Absolute Confidence

Step 2 - What does the negative voice say that tells you this is not possible? _____
_____

Step 3 - How do you feel when you hear this negative voice (find ONE word)? _____

Step 4 - Where do you feel this in your body? _____

Step 5 - Drift back to an earlier time when you felt the same way - get a snapshot or a movie. (Circle One)

     Snapshot   Movie   No Image

Notes on previous memory _____
_____
_____

Step 6 - Smell Memory Release Blend or other oils - specify which oils used: _____

Step 7 - Notice changes: _____
_____
_____

Step 8 - Is there a new belief or mindset that has emerged? _____
_____
_____

Step 9 - Read the original intention and rate it again - how possible does it feel now? (circle one)

     Zero Hope - 0 1 2 3 4 5 6 7 8 9 10 - Absolute Confidence

(If 8 or higher (or if no negative voice), skip to Step 10 - the Affirmation. If less than 8, return to Step 2 on next page.)

How far have you shifted thus far?

Starting number: _____ New Number: _____

Step 2 - Re-read the intention and listen for what else the negative voice says about why it can't happen. _____

_____

Step 3 - How do you feel when you hear the negative voice? (find ONE word) _____

Step 4 - Where do you feel this in your body? _____

_____

Step 5 - Drift back to an earlier time when you felt the same way - get a snapshot or a movie. (Circle One)

Snapshot   Movie   No Image

Notes on previous memory: _____

_____

Step 6 - Smell Memory Release Blend or other oils - specify which oils used: _____

Step 7 - Notice changes _____

_____

Step 8 - Is there a new belief or mindset that has emerged? _____

_____

Step 9 - Read the original intention and rate it again - how possible does it feel now? (circle)

Zero Hope - 0 1 2 3 4 5 6 7 8 9 10 - Absolute Confidence

Look how far you've shifted!

Starting number: _____ Second Number: _____

Final Number: _____

(Move forward to Step 10 - the Affirmation - even if you're not yet at an 8 or higher. More shifting will occur during the next 3 steps.)

Step 10 - Affirmation: _____

_____

_____
_____

Step 11 - Stand in Power Pose: Repeat the affirmation for 2 minutes, twice daily, with conviction while standing in a power pose. Smell *Believe*™ or *Transformation*™ Oil Blend as you do this. (You may choose another transforming oil if you'd like, such as *Build Your Dream*™, *Magnify Your Purpose*™, etc)

Repeat for _at least three consecutive days,_ or until you create a new affirmation. Check off each box when complete.

Always make sure that your energy feels clear when you say the statement. If you experience inner resistance, use the AFT process to identify and release any negative thoughts, feelings, or memories that come up.

Date	AM	PM

Step 12 - Make Your Plan of Action: _____

_____
_____
_____
_____
_____
_____

Follow-up - What has changed in your life because of THIS Aroma Freedom Technique Session? _____

_____
_____
_____
_____
_____
_____
_____
_____
_____
_____
_____
_____
_____
_____
_____
_____
_____
_____
_____

Program your mind daily! As soon as one affirmation is complete or the goal has been reached, create another. Make affirmations a daily habit and soon you will not feel right unless you have done your daily practice. This will keep you focused in the direction of your dreams. Feel free to experiment with different oils as you progress.

Date of Personal AFT Session: _____

Step 1 - Set Your Intention: _____

_____

_____

Rating your intention. How possible does it feel? (Circle One)

Zero Hope - 0 1 2 3 4 5 6 7 8 9 10 - Absolute Confidence

Step 2 - What does the negative voice say that tells you this is not possible? _____

_____

Step 3 - How do you feel when you hear this negative voice (find ONE word)? _____

Step 4 - Where do you feel this in your body? _____

_____

Step 5 - Drift back to an earlier time when you felt the same way - get a snapshot or a movie. (Circle One)

Snapshot   Movie   No Image

Notes on previous memory _____

_____

_____

Step 6 - Smell Memory Release Blend or other oils - specify which oils used: _____

Step 7 - Notice changes: _____

_____

_____

Step 8 - Is there a new belief or mindset that has emerged? _____

_____

_____

Step 9 - Read the original intention and rate it again - how possible does it feel now? (circle one)

Zero Hope - 0 1 2 3 4 5 6 7 8 9 10 - Absolute Confidence

(If 8 or higher (or if no negative voice), skip to Step 10 - the Affirmation. If less than 8, return to Step 2 on next page.)

How far have you shifted thus far?

    Starting number: _____ New Number: _____

Step 2 - Re-read the intention and listen for what else the negative voice says about why it can't happen. _____

_____

Step 3 - How do you feel when you hear the negative voice? (find ONE word) _____

Step 4 - Where do you feel this in your body? _____

_____

_____

Step 5 - Drift back to an earlier time when you felt the same way - get a snapshot or a movie. (Circle One)

    Snapshot Movie No Image

Notes on previous memory: _____

_____

_____

Step 6 - Smell Memory Release Blend or other oils - specify which oils used: _____

Step 7 - Notice changes _____

_____

_____

Step 8 - Is there a new belief or mindset that has emerged? _____

_____

_____

Step 9 - Read the original intention and rate it again - how possible does it feel now? (circle)

  Zero Hope - 0 1 2 3 4 5 6 7 8 9 10 - Absolute Confidence

Look how far you've shifted!

    Starting number: _____ Second Number: _____
        Final Number: _____

(Move forward to Step 10 - the Affirmation - even if you're not yet at an 8 or higher. More shifting will occur during the next 3 steps.)

Step 10 - Affirmation: _____

_____

_____

_____

Step 11 - Stand in Power Pose: Repeat the affirmation for 2 minutes, twice daily, with conviction while standing in a power pose. Smell *Believe*™ or *Transformation*™ Oil Blend as you do this. (You may choose another transforming oil if you'd like, such as *Build Your Dream*™, *Magnify Your Purpose*™, etc)

Repeat for *at least three consecutive days*, or until you create a new affirmation. Check off each box when complete.

Always make sure that your energy feels clear when you say the statement. If you experience inner resistance, use the AFT process to identify and release any negative thoughts, feelings, or memories that come up.

Date	AM	PM

Step 12 - Make Your Plan of Action: _____

_____

_____

_____

_____

_____

Follow-up - What has changed in your life because of THIS Aroma Freedom Technique Session? _____

_____

_____

_____

_____

_____

_____

_____

_____

_____

_____

_____

_____

_____

_____

_____

_____

_____

_____

_____

Program your mind daily! As soon as one affirmation is complete or the goal has been reached, create another. Make affirmations a daily habit and soon you will not feel right unless you have done your daily practice. This will keep you focused in the direction of your dreams. Feel free to experiment with different oils as you progress.

Date of Personal AFT Session: _____

Step 1 - Set Your Intention: _____
_____

Rating your intention. How possible does it feel? (Circle One)

      Zero Hope - 0 1 2 3 4 5 6 7 8 9 10 - Absolute Confidence

Step 2 - What does the negative voice say that tells you this is not possible? _____
_____

Step 3 - How do you feel when you hear this negative voice (find ONE word)? _____

Step 4 - Where do you feel this in your body? _____

Step 5 - Drift back to an earlier time when you felt the same way - get a snapshot or a movie. (Circle One)

      Snapshot   Movie   No Image

Notes on previous memory _____
_____

Step 6 - Smell Memory Release Blend or other oils - specify which oils used: _____

Step 7 - Notice changes: _____
_____

Step 8 - Is there a new belief or mindset that has emerged? _____
_____

Step 9 - Read the original intention and rate it again - how possible does it feel now? (circle one)

      Zero Hope - 0 1 2 3 4 5 6 7 8 9 10 - Absolute Confidence

(If 8 or higher (or if no negative voice), skip to Step 10 - the Affirmation. If less than 8, return to Step 2 on next page.)

How far have you shifted thus far?

Starting number: _____ New Number: _____

Step 2 - Re-read the intention and listen for what else the negative voice says about why it can't happen. _____

_____

Step 3 - How do you feel when you hear the negative voice? (find ONE word) _____

Step 4 - Where do you feel this in your body? _____

_____

Step 5 - Drift back to an earlier time when you felt the same way - get a snapshot or a movie. (Circle One)

Snapshot   Movie   No Image

Notes on previous memory: _____

_____

Step 6 - Smell Memory Release Blend or other oils - specify which oils used: _____

Step 7 - Notice changes _____

_____

Step 8 - Is there a new belief or mindset that has emerged? _____

_____

Step 9 - Read the original intention and rate it again - how possible does it feel now? (circle)

Zero Hope - 0 1 2 3 4 5 6 7 8 9 10 - Absolute Confidence

Look how far you've shifted!

Starting number: _____ Second Number: _____

Final Number: _____

(Move forward to Step 10 - the Affirmation - even if you're not yet at an 8 or higher. More shifting will occur during the next 3 steps.)

Step 10 - Affirmation: _____

_____

_____

_____

Step 11 - Stand in Power Pose: Repeat the affirmation for 2 minutes, twice daily, with conviction while standing in a power pose. Smell *Relieve*™ or *Transformation*™ Oil Blend as you do this. (You may choose another transforming oil if you'd like, such as *Build Your Dream*™, *Magnify Your Purpose*™, etc)

Repeat for *at least three consecutive days,* or until you create a new affirmation. Check off each box when complete.

Always make sure that your energy feels clear when you say the statement. If you experience inner resistance, use the AFT process to identify and release any negative thoughts, feelings, or memories that come up.

Date	AM	PM

Step 12 - Make Your Plan of Action: _____

_____

_____

_____

_____

_____

Follow-up - What has changed in your life because of THIS Aroma Freedom Technique Session? _____

_____

_____

_____

_____

_____

_____

_____

_____

_____

_____

_____

_____

_____

_____

_____

_____

_____

_____

Program your mind daily! As soon as one affirmation is complete or the goal has been reached, create another. Make affirmations a daily habit and soon you will not feel right unless you have done your daily practice. This will keep you focused in the direction of your dreams. Feel free to experiment with different oils as you progress.

Date of Personal AFT Session: _____

Step 1 - Set Your Intention: _____

_____

Rating your intention. How possible does it feel? (Circle One)

    Zero Hope - 0 1 2 3 4 5 6 7 8 9 10 - Absolute Confidence

Step 2 - What does the negative voice say that tells you this is not possible? _____

_____

Step 3 - How do you feel when you hear this negative voice (find ONE word)? _____

Step 4 - Where do you feel this in your body? _____

_____

Step 5 - Drift back to an earlier time when you felt the same way - get a snapshot or a movie. (Circle One)

    Snapshot   Movie   No Image

Notes on previous memory _____

_____

Step 6 - Smell Memory Release Blend or other oils - specify which oils used: _____

Step 7 - Notice changes: _____

_____

Step 8 - Is there a new belief or mindset that has emerged? _____

_____

Step 9 - Read the original intention and rate it again - how possible does it feel now? (circle one)

    Zero Hope - 0 1 2 3 4 5 6 7 8 9 10 - Absolute Confidence

(If 8 or higher (or if no negative voice), skip to Step 10 - the Affirmation. If less than 8, return to Step 2 on next page.)

How far have you shifted thus far?

Starting number: _____ New Number: _____

Step 2 - Re-read the intention and listen for what else the negative voice says about why it can't happen. _____

_____

Step 3 - How do you feel when you hear the negative voice? (find ONE word) _____

Step 4 - Where do you feel this in your body? _____

_____

Step 5 - Drift back to an earlier time when you felt the same way - get a snapshot or a movie. (Circle One)

Snapshot   Movie   No Image

Notes on previous memory: _____

_____

Step 6 - Smell Memory Release Blend or other oils - specify which oils used: _____

Step 7 - Notice changes _____

_____

Step 8 - Is there a new belief or mindset that has emerged? _____

_____

Step 9 - Read the original intention and rate it again - how possible does it feel now? (circle)

Zero Hope - 0 1 2 3 4 5 6 7 8 9 10 - Absolute Confidence

Look how far you've shifted!

Starting number: _____ Second Number: _____

Final Number: _____

(Move forward to Step 10 - the Affirmation - even if you're not yet at an 8 or higher. More shifting will occur during the next 3 steps.)

Step 10 - Affirmation: _____

_____
_____
_____

Step 11 - Stand in Power Pose: Repeat the affirmation for 2 minutes, twice daily, with conviction while standing in a power pose. Smell *Believe*™ or *Transformation*™ Oil Blend as you do this. (You may choose another transforming oil if you'd like, such as *Build Your Dream*™, *Magnify Your Purpose*™, etc)

Repeat for *at least three consecutive days*, or until you create a new affirmation. Check off each box when complete.

Always make sure that your energy feels clear when you say the statement. If you experience inner resistance, use the AFT process to identify and release any negative thoughts, feelings, or memories that come up.

Date	AM	PM

Step 12 - Make Your Plan of Action: _____

_____
_____
_____
_____
_____
_____

Follow-up - What has changed in your life because of THIS Aroma Freedom Technique Session? _____

_____

_____

_____

_____

_____

_____

_____

_____

_____

_____

_____

_____

_____

_____

_____

_____

_____

_____

_____

Program your mind daily! As soon as one affirmation is complete or the goal has been reached, create another. Make affirmations a daily habit and soon you will not feel right unless you have done your daily practice. This will keep you focused in the direction of your dreams. Feel free to experiment with different oils as you progress.

Date of Personal AFT Session: _____

Step 1 - Set Your Intention: _____
_____
_____

Rating your intention. How possible does it feel? (Circle One)

    Zero Hope   0 1 2 3 4 5 6 7 8 9 10 - Absolute Confidence

Step 2 - What does the negative voice say that tells you this is not possible? _____
_____

Step 3 - How do you feel when you hear this negative voice (find ONE word)? _____

Step 4 - Where do you feel this in your body? _____

Step 5 - Drift back to an earlier time when you felt the same way - get a snapshot or a movie. (Circle One)

       Snapshot   Movie   No Image

Notes on previous memory _____
_____
_____

Step 6 - Smell Memory Release Blend or other oils - specify which oils used: _____

Step 7 - Notice changes: _____
_____
_____

Step 8 - Is there a new belief or mindset that has emerged? _____
_____
_____

Step 9 - Read the original intention and rate it again - how possible does it feel now? (circle one)

    Zero Hope - 0 1 2 3 4 5 6 7 8 9 10 - Absolute Confidence

(If 8 or higher (or if no negative voice), skip to Step 10 - the Affirmation. If less than 8, return to Step 2 on next page.)

How far have you shifted thus far?

        Starting number: _____ New Number: _____

Step 2 - Re-read the intention and listen for what else the negative voice says about why it can't happen. _____

_____

Step 3 - How do you feel when you hear the negative voice? (find ONE word) _____

Step 4 - Where do you feel this in your body? _____

_____

Step 5 - Drift back to an earlier time when you felt the same way - get a snapshot or a movie. (Circle One)

        Snapshot   Movie   No Image

Notes on previous memory: _____

_____

Step 6 - Smell Memory Release Blend or other oils - specify which oils used: _____

Step 7 - Notice changes _____

_____

Step 8 - Is there a new belief or mindset that has emerged? _____

_____

Step 9 - Read the original intention and rate it again - how possible does it feel now? (circle)

      Zero Hope - 0 1 2 3 4 5 6 7 8 9 10 - Absolute Confidence

Look how far you've shifted!

        Starting number: _____ Second Number: _____

              Final Number: _____

(Move forward to Step 10 - the Affirmation - even if you're not yet at an 8 or higher. More shifting will occur during the next 3 steps.)

Step 10 - Affirmation: _____

_____

_____

_____

Step 11 - Stand in Power Pose: Repeat the affirmation for 2 minutes, twice daily, with conviction while standing in a power pose. Smell *Believe*™ or *Transformation*™ Oil Blend as you do this. (You may choose another transforming oil if you'd like, such as *Build Your Dream*™, *Magnify Your Purpose*™, etc)

Repeat for *at least three consecutive days,* or until you create a new affirmation. Check off each box when complete.

Always make sure that your energy feels clear when you say the statement. If you experience inner resistance, use the AFT process to identify and release any negative thoughts, feelings, or memories that come up.

Date	AM	PM

Step 12 - Make Your Plan of Action: _____

_____

_____

_____

_____

_____

Follow-up - What has changed in your life because of THIS Aroma Freedom Technique Session? _____

_____

_____

_____

_____

_____

_____

_____

_____

_____

_____

_____

_____

_____

_____

_____

_____

_____

_____

_____

_____

Program your mind daily! As soon as one affirmation is complete or the goal has been reached, create another. Make affirmations a daily habit and soon you will not feel right unless you have done your daily practice. This will keep you focused in the direction of your dreams. Feel free to experiment with different oils as you progress.

Date of Personal AFT Session: _____

Step 1 - Set Your Intention: _____

_____

_____

Rating your intention. How possible does it feel? (Circle One)

Zero Hope - 0 1 2 3 4 5 6 7 8 9 10 - Absolute Confidence

Step 2 - What does the negative voice say that tells you this is not possible? _____

_____

Step 3 - How do you feel when you hear this negative voice (find ONE word)? _____

Step 4 - Where do you feel this in your body? _____

_____

Step 5 - Drift back to an earlier time when you felt the same way - get a snapshot or a movie. (Circle One)

Snapshot   Movie   No Image

Notes on previous memory _____

_____

_____

Step 6 - Smell Memory Release Blend or other oils - specify which oils used: _____

Step 7 - Notice changes: _____

_____

_____

Step 8 - Is there a new belief or mindset that has emerged? _____

_____

_____

Step 9 - Read the original intention and rate it again - how possible does it feel now? (circle one)

Zero Hope - 0 1 2 3 4 5 6 7 8 9 10 - Absolute Confidence

(If 8 or higher (or if no negative voice), skip to Step 10 - the Affirmation. If less than 8, return to Step 2 on next page.)

How far have you shifted thus far?

Starting number: _____ New Number: _____

Step 2 - Re-read the intention and listen for what else the negative voice says about why it can't happen. _____

_____

Step 3 - How do you feel when you hear the negative voice? (find ONE word) _____

Step 4 - Where do you feel this in your body? _____

_____

Step 5 - Drift back to an earlier time when you felt the same way - get a snapshot or a movie. (Circle One)

Snapshot   Movie   No Image

Notes on previous memory: _____

_____

Step 6 - Smell Memory Release Blend or other oils - specify which oils used: _____

Step 7 - Notice changes _____

_____

Step 8 - Is there a new belief or mindset that has emerged? _____

_____

Step 9 - Read the original intention and rate it again - how possible does it feel now? (circle)

Zero Hope - 0 1 2 3 4 5 6 7 8 9 10 - Absolute Confidence

Look how far you've shifted!

Starting number: _____ Second Number: _____

Final Number: _____

(Move forward to Step 10 - the Affirmation - even if you're not yet at an 8 or higher. More shifting will occur during the next 3 steps.)

Step 10 - Affirmation: _____

_____

_____

_____

Step 11 - Stand in Power Pose: Repeat the affirmation for 2 minutes, twice daily, with conviction while standing in a power pose. Smell *Relieve*™ or *Transformation*™ Oil Blend as you do this. (You may choose another transforming oil if you'd like, such as *Build Your Dream*™, *Magnify Your Purpose*™, etc)

Repeat for *at least three consecutive days,* or until you create a new affirmation. Check off each box when complete.

Always make sure that your energy feels clear when you say the statement. If you experience inner resistance, use the AFT process to identify and release any negative thoughts, feelings, or memories that come up.

Date	AM	PM

Step 12 - Make Your Plan of Action: _____

_____

_____

_____

_____

_____

Follow-up - What has changed in your life because of THIS Aroma Freedom Technique Session? _____

_____
_____
_____
_____
_____
_____
_____
_____
_____
_____
_____
_____
_____
_____
_____
_____
_____
_____
_____

Program your mind daily! As soon as one affirmation is complete or the goal has been reached, create another. Make affirmations a daily habit and soon you will not feel right unless you have done your daily practice. This will keep you focused in the direction of your dreams. Feel free to experiment with different oils as you progress.

Date of Personal AFT Session: _____

Step 1 - Set Your Intention: _____

_____

Rating your intention. How possible does it feel? (Circle One)

    Zero Hope - 0 1 2 3 4 5 6 7 8 9 10 - Absolute Confidence

Step 2 - What does the negative voice say that tells you this is not possible? _____

_____

Step 3 - How do you feel when you hear this negative voice (find ONE word)? _____

Step 4 - Where do you feel this in your body? _____

Step 5 - Drift back to an earlier time when you felt the same way - get a snapshot or a movie. (Circle One)

        Snapshot   Movie   No Image

Notes on previous memory _____

_____

Step 6 - Smell Memory Release Blend or other oils - specify which oils used: _____

Step 7 - Notice changes: _____

_____

Step 8 - Is there a new belief or mindset that has emerged? _____

_____

Step 9 - Read the original intention and rate it again - how possible does it feel now? (circle one)

    Zero Hope - 0 1 2 3 4 5 6 7 8 9 10 - Absolute Confidence

(If 8 or higher (or if no negative voice), skip to Step 10 - the Affirmation. If less than 8, return to Step 2 on next page.)

How far have you shifted thus far?

Starting number: _____ New Number: _____

Step 2 - Re-read the intention and listen for what else the negative voice says about why it can't happen. _____

_____

Step 3 - How do you feel when you hear the negative voice? (find ONE word) _____

Step 4 - Where do you feel this in your body? _____

_____

Step 5 - Drift back to an earlier time when you felt the same way - get a snapshot or a movie. (Circle One)

Snapshot   Movie   No Image

Notes on previous memory: _____

_____

Step 6 - Smell Memory Release Blend or other oils - specify which oils used: _____

Step 7 - Notice changes _____

_____

_____

Step 8 - Is there a new belief or mindset that has emerged? _____

_____

_____

Step 9 - Read the original intention and rate it again - how possible does it feel now? (circle)

Zero Hope - 0 1 2 3 4 5 6 7 8 9 10 - Absolute Confidence

Look how far you've shifted!

Starting number: _____ Second Number: _____

Final Number: _____

(Move forward to Step 10 - the Affirmation - even if you're not yet at an 8 or higher. More shifting will occur during the next 3 steps.)

Step 10 - Affirmation: _____

_____

_____

_____

Step 11 - Stand in Power Pose: Repeat the affirmation for 2 minutes, twice daily, with conviction while standing in a power pose. Smell *Relieve*™ or *Transformation*™ Oil Blend as you do this. (You may choose another transforming oil if you'd like, such as *Build Your Dream*™, *Magnify Your Purpose*™, etc)

Repeat for <u>at least three consecutive days</u>, or until you create a new affirmation. Check off each box when complete.

Always make sure that your energy feels clear when you say the statement. If you experience inner resistance, use the AFT process to identify and release any negative thoughts, feelings, or memories that come up.

Date	AM	PM

Step 12 - Make Your Plan of Action: _____

_____

_____

_____

_____

115

Follow-up - What has changed in your life because of THIS Aroma Freedom Technique Session? _____

_____
_____
_____
_____
_____
_____
_____
_____
_____
_____
_____
_____
_____
_____
_____
_____
_____
_____
_____

Program your mind daily! As soon as one affirmation is complete or the goal has been reached, create another. Make affirmations a daily habit and soon you will not feel right unless you have done your daily practice. This will keep you focused in the direction of your dreams. Feel free to experiment with different oils as you progress.

Date of Personal AFT Session: _____

Step 1 - Set Your Intention: _____
_____
_____

Rating your intention. How possible does it feel? (Circle One)

    Zero Hope - 0 1 2 3 4 5 6 7 8 9 10 - Absolute Confidence

Step 2 - What does the negative voice say that tells you this is not possible? _____
_____

Step 3 - How do you feel when you hear this negative voice (find ONE word)? _____

Step 4 - Where do you feel this in your body? _____

Step 5 - Drift back to an earlier time when you felt the same way - get a snapshot or a movie. (Circle One)

       Snapshot   Movie   No Image

Notes on previous memory _____
_____
_____

Step 6 - Smell Memory Release Blend or other oils - specify which oils used: _____

Step 7 - Notice changes: _____
_____
_____

Step 8 - Is there a new belief or mindset that has emerged? _____
_____
_____

Step 9 - Read the original intention and rate it again - how possible does it feel now? (circle one)

    Zero Hope - 0 1 2 3 4 5 6 7 8 9 10 - Absolute Confidence

(If 8 or higher (or if no negative voice), skip to Step 10 - the Affirmation. If less than 8, return to Step 2 on next page.)

How far have you shifted thus far?

Starting number: _____ New Number: _____

Step 2 - Re-read the intention and listen for what else the negative voice says about why it can't happen. _____

_____

Step 3 - How do you feel when you hear the negative voice? (find ONE word) _____

Step 4 - Where do you feel this in your body? _____

_____

Step 5 - Drift back to an earlier time when you felt the same way - get a snapshot or a movie. (Circle One)

Snapshot   Movie   No Image

Notes on previous memory: _____

_____

Step 6 - Smell Memory Release Blend or other oils - specify which oils used: _____

Step 7 - Notice changes _____

_____

Step 8 - Is there a new belief or mindset that has emerged? _____

_____

Step 9 - Read the original intention and rate it again - how possible does it feel now? (circle)

Zero Hope - 0 1 2 3 4 5 6 7 8 9 10 - Absolute Confidence

Look how far you've shifted!

Starting number: _____ Second Number: _____

Final Number: _____

(Move forward to Step 10 - the Affirmation - even if you're not yet at an 8 or higher. More shifting will occur during the next 3 steps.)

Step 10 - Affirmation: _____

_____

_____

_____

Step 11 - Stand in Power Pose: Repeat the affirmation for 2 minutes, twice daily, with conviction while standing in a power pose. Smell *Believe*™ or *Transformation*™ Oil Blend as you do this. (You may choose another transforming oil if you'd like, such as *Build Your Dream*™, *Magnify Your Purpose*™, etc)

Repeat for *at least three consecutive days*, or until you create a new affirmation. Check off each box when complete.

Always make sure that your energy feels clear when you say the statement. If you experience inner resistance, use the AFT process to identify and release any negative thoughts, feelings, or memories that come up.

Date	AM	PM

Step 12 - Make Your Plan of Action: _____

_____

_____

_____

_____

_____

Follow-up - What has changed in your life because of THIS Aroma Freedom Technique Session? _____

_____

_____

_____

_____

_____

_____

_____

_____

_____

_____

_____

_____

_____

_____

_____

_____

_____

_____

Program your mind daily! As soon as one affirmation is complete or the goal has been reached, create another. Make affirmations a daily habit and soon you will not feel right unless you have done your daily practice. This will keep you focused in the direction of your dreams. Feel free to experiment with different oils as you progress.

Date of Personal AFT Session: _____

Step 1 - Set Your Intention: _____
_____
_____

Rating your intention. How possible does it feel? (Circle One)

Zero Hope - 0 1 2 3 4 5 6 7 8 9 10 - Absolute Confidence

Step 2 - What does the negative voice say that tells you this is not possible? _____
_____

Step 3 - How do you feel when you hear this negative voice (find ONE word)? _____

Step 4 - Where do you feel this in your body? _____

Step 5 - Drift back to an earlier time when you felt the same way - get a snapshot or a movie. (Circle One)

Snapshot   Movie   No Image

Notes on previous memory _____
_____
_____

Step 6 - Smell Memory Release Blend or other oils - specify which oils used: _____

Step 7 - Notice changes: _____
_____
_____

Step 8 - Is there a new belief or mindset that has emerged? _____
_____
_____

Step 9 - Read the original intention and rate it again - how possible does it feel now? (circle one)

Zero Hope - 0 1 2 3 4 5 6 7 8 9 10 - Absolute Confidence

(If 8 or higher (or if no negative voice), skip to Step 10 - the Affirmation. If less than 8, return to Step 2 on next page.)

121

How far have you shifted thus far?

Starting number: _____ New Number: _____

Step 2 - Re-read the intention and listen for what else the negative voice says about why it can't happen. _____

_____

Step 3 - How do you feel when you hear the negative voice? (find ONE word) _____

Step 4 - Where do you feel this in your body? _____

_____

Step 5 - Drift back to an earlier time when you felt the same way - get a snapshot or a movie. (Circle One)

Snapshot   Movie   No Image

Notes on previous memory: _____

_____

Step 6 - Smell Memory Release Blend or other oils - specify which oils used: _____

Step 7 - Notice changes _____

_____

Step 8 - Is there a new belief or mindset that has emerged? _____

_____

Step 9 - Read the original intention and rate it again - how possible does it feel now? (circle)

Zero Hope - 0 1 2 3 4 5 6 7 8 9 10 - Absolute Confidence

Look how far you've shifted!

Starting number: _____ Second Number: _____

Final Number: _____

(Move forward to Step 10 - the Affirmation - even if you're not yet at an 8 or higher. More shifting will occur during the next 3 steps.)

Step 10 - Affirmation: _____

_____
_____
_____

Step 11 - Stand in Power Pose: Repeat the affirmation for 2 minutes, twice daily, with conviction while standing in a power pose. Smell *Believe*™ or *Transformation*™ Oil Blend as you do this. (You may choose another transforming oil if you'd like, such as *Build Your Dream*™, *Magnify Your Purpose*™, etc)

Repeat for _at least three consecutive days_, or until you create a new affirmation. Check off each box when complete.

Always make sure that your energy feels clear when you say the statement. If you experience inner resistance, use the AFT process to identify and release any negative thoughts, feelings, or memories that come up.

Date	AM	PM

Step 12 - Make Your Plan of Action: _____

_____
_____
_____
_____
_____

Follow-up - What has changed in your life because of THIS Aroma Freedom Technique Session? _____

_____

_____

_____

_____

_____

_____

_____

_____

_____

_____

_____

_____

_____

_____

_____

_____

_____

_____

Program your mind daily! As soon as one affirmation is complete or the goal has been reached, create another. Make affirmations a daily habit and soon you will not feel right unless you have done your daily practice. This will keep you focused in the direction of your dreams. Feel free to experiment with different oils as you progress.

Date of Personal AFT Session: _____

Step 1 - Set Your Intention: _____

_____

Rating your intention. How possible does it feel? (Circle One)

Zero Hope - 0 1 2 3 4 5 6 7 8 9 10 - Absolute Confidence

Step 2 - What does the negative voice say that tells you this is not possible? _____

Step 3 - How do you feel when you hear this negative voice (find ONE word)? _____

Step 4 - Where do you feel this in your body? _____

Step 5 - Drift back to an earlier time when you felt the same way - get a snapshot or a movie. (Circle One)

Snapshot   Movie   No Image

Notes on previous memory _____

_____

Step 6 - Smell Memory Release Blend or other oils - specify which oils used: _____

Step 7 - Notice changes: _____

_____

Step 8 - Is there a new belief or mindset that has emerged? _____

_____

Step 9 - Read the original intention and rate it again - how possible does it feel now? (circle one)

Zero Hope - 0 1 2 3 4 5 6 7 8 9 10 - Absolute Confidence

(If 8 or higher (or if no negative voice), skip to Step 10 - the Affirmation. If less than 8, return to Step 2 on next page.)

How far have you shifted thus far?

Starting number: _____ New Number: _____

Step 2 - Re-read the intention and listen for what else the negative voice says about why it can't happen. _____

_____

Step 3 - How do you feel when you hear the negative voice? (find ONE word) _____

Step 4 - Where do you feel this in your body? _____

_____

Step 5 - Drift back to an earlier time when you felt the same way - get a snapshot or a movie. (Circle One)

Snapshot   Movie   No Image

Notes on previous memory: _____

_____

Step 6 - Smell Memory Release Blend or other oils - specify which oils used: _____

Step 7 - Notice changes _____

_____

Step 8 - Is there a new belief or mindset that has emerged? _____

_____

Step 9 - Read the original intention and rate it again - how possible does it feel now? (circle)

Zero Hope - 0 1 2 3 4 5 6 7 8 9 10 - Absolute Confidence

Look how far you've shifted!

Starting number: _____ Second Number: _____

Final Number: _____

(Move forward to Step 10 - the Affirmation - even if you're not yet at an 8 or higher. More shifting will occur during the next 3 steps.)

Step 10 - Affirmation: _____

_____

_____

_____

Step 11 - Stand in Power Pose: Repeat the affirmation for 2 minutes, twice daily, with conviction while standing in a power pose. Smell *Believe*™ or *Transformation*™ Oil Blend as you do this. (You may choose another transforming oil if you'd like, such as *Build Your Dream*™, *Magnify Your Purpose*™, etc)

Repeat for _at least three consecutive days,_ or until you create a new affirmation. Check off each box when complete.

Always make sure that your energy feels clear when you say the statement. If you experience inner resistance, use the AFT process to identify and release any negative thoughts, feelings, or memories that come up.

Date	AM	PM

Step 12 - Make Your Plan of Action: _____

_____

_____

_____

_____

_____

_____

Follow-up - What has changed in your life because of THIS Aroma Freedom Technique Session? _____

_____

_____

_____

_____

_____

_____

_____

_____

_____

_____

_____

_____

_____

_____

_____

_____

_____

Program your mind daily! As soon as one affirmation is complete or the goal has been reached, create another. Make affirmations a daily habit and soon you will not feel right unless you have done your daily practice. This will keep you focused in the direction of your dreams. Feel free to experiment with different oils as you progress.

Date of Personal AFT Session: _____

Step 1 - Set Your Intention: _____

_____

_____

Rating your intention. How possible does it feel? (Circle One)

    Zero Hope - 0 1 2 3 4 5 6 7 8 9 10 - Absolute Confidence

Step 2 - What does the negative voice say that tells you this is not possible? _____

_____

Step 3 - How do you feel when you hear this negative voice (find ONE word)? _____

Step 4 - Where do you feel this in your body? _____

Step 5 - Drift back to an earlier time when you felt the same way - get a snapshot or a movie. (Circle One)

        Snapshot   Movie   No Image

Notes on previous memory _____

_____

_____

Step 6 - Smell Memory Release Blend or other oils - specify which oils used: _____

Step 7 - Notice changes: _____

_____

_____

Step 8 - Is there a new belief or mindset that has emerged? _____

_____

_____

Step 9 - Read the original intention and rate it again - how possible does it feel now? (circle one)

    Zero Hope - 0 1 2 3 4 5 6 7 8 9 10 - Absolute Confidence

(If 8 or higher (or if no negative voice), skip to Step 10 - the Affirmation. If less than 8, return to Step 2 on next page.)

How far have you shifted thus far?

　　　　　　Starting number: _____ New Number: _____

Step 2 - Re-read the intention and listen for what else the negative voice says about why it can't happen. _____

_____

Step 3 - How do you feel when you hear the negative voice? (find ONE word) _____

Step 4 - Where do you feel this in your body? _____

_____

Step 5 - Drift back to an earlier time when you felt the same way - get a snapshot or a movie. (Circle One)

　　　　Snapshot　　　Movie　　　No Image

Notes on previous memory: _____

_____

Step 6 - Smell Memory Release Blend or other oils - specify which oils used: _____

Step 7 - Notice changes _____

_____

Step 8 - Is there a new belief or mindset that has emerged? _____

_____

Step 9 - Read the original intention and rate it again - how possible does it feel now? (circle)

　　Zero Hope - 0 1 2 3 4 5 6 7 8 9 10 - Absolute Confidence

Look how far you've shifted!

　　　　　　Starting number: _____ Second Number: _____
　　　　　　　　　Final Number: _____

(Move forward to Step 10 - the Affirmation - even if you're not yet at an 8 or higher. More shifting will occur during the next 3 steps.)

Step 10 - Affirmation: _____

_____

_____

_____

Step 11 - Stand in Power Pose: Repeat the affirmation for 2 minutes, twice daily, with conviction while standing in a power pose. Smell _Believe_™ or _Transformation_™ Oil Blend as you do this. (You may choose another transforming oil if you'd like, such as _Build Your Dream_™, _Magnify Your Purpose_™, etc)

Repeat for _at least three consecutive days_, or until you create a new affirmation. Check off each box when complete.

Always make sure that your energy feels clear when you say the statement. If you experience inner resistance, use the AFT process to identify and release any negative thoughts, feelings, or memories that come up.

Date	AM	PM

Step 12 - Make Your Plan of Action: _____

_____

_____

_____

_____

_____

Follow-up - What has changed in your life because of THIS Aroma Freedom Technique Session? _____

_____

_____

_____

_____

_____

_____

_____

_____

_____

_____

_____

_____

_____

_____

_____

_____

_____

_____

_____

Program your mind daily! As soon as one affirmation is complete or the goal has been reached, create another. Make affirmations a daily habit and soon you will not feel right unless you have done your daily practice. This will keep you focused in the direction of your dreams. Feel free to experiment with different oils as you progress.

Date of Personal AFT Session: _____

Step 1 - Set Your Intention: _____
_____

Rating your intention. How possible does it feel? (Circle One)

    Zero Hope - 0 1 2 3 4 5 6 7 8 9 10 - Absolute Confidence

Step 2 - What does the negative voice say that tells you this is not possible? _____
_____

Step 3 - How do you feel when you hear this negative voice (find ONE word)? _____

Step 4 - Where do you feel this in your body? _____

Step 5 - Drift back to an earlier time when you felt the same way - get a snapshot or a movie. (Circle One)

    Snapshot   Movie   No Image

Notes on previous memory _____
_____

Step 6 - Smell Memory Release Blend or other oils - specify which oils used: _____

Step 7 - Notice changes: _____
_____

Step 8 - Is there a new belief or mindset that has emerged? _____
_____

Step 9 - Read the original intention and rate it again - how possible does it feel now? (circle one)

    Zero Hope - 0 1 2 3 4 5 6 7 8 9 10 - Absolute Confidence

(If 8 or higher (or if no negative voice), skip to Step 10 - the Affirmation. If less than 8, return to Step 2 on next page.)

How far have you shifted thus far?

Starting number: _____ New Number: _____

Step 2 - Re-read the intention and listen for what else the negative voice says about why it can't happen. _____

_____

Step 3 - How do you feel when you hear the negative voice? (find ONE word) _____

Step 4 - Where do you feel this in your body? _____

_____

_____

Step 5 - Drift back to an earlier time when you felt the same way - get a snapshot or a movie. (Circle One)

Snapshot   Movie   No Image

Notes on previous memory: _____

_____

_____

Step 6 - Smell Memory Release Blend or other oils - specify which oils used: _____

Step 7 - Notice changes _____

_____

_____

Step 8 - Is there a new belief or mindset that has emerged? _____

_____

_____

Step 9 - Read the original intention and rate it again - how possible does it feel now? (circle)

Zero Hope - 0 1 2 3 4 5 6 7 8 9 10 - Absolute Confidence

Look how far you've shifted!

Starting number: _____ Second Number: _____

Final Number: _____

(Move forward to Step 10 - the Affirmation - even if you're not yet at an 8 or higher. More shifting will occur during the next 3 steps.)

Step 10 - Affirmation: _____

_____

_____

_____

Step 11 - Stand in Power Pose: Repeat the affirmation for 2 minutes, twice daily, with conviction while standing in a power pose. Smell _Believe_™ or _Transformation_™ Oil Blend as you do this. (You may choose another transforming oil if you'd like, such as _Build Your Dream_™, _Magnify Your Purpose_™, etc)

Repeat for _at least three consecutive days_, or until you create a new affirmation. Check off each box when complete.

Always make sure that your energy feels clear when you say the statement. If you experience inner resistance, use the AFT process to identify and release any negative thoughts, feelings, or memories that come up.

Date	AM	PM

Step 12 - Make Your Plan of Action: _____

_____

_____

_____

_____

_____

Follow-up - What has changed in your life because of THIS Aroma Freedom Technique Session? _____

_____

_____

_____

_____

_____

_____

_____

_____

_____

_____

_____

_____

_____

_____

_____

_____

_____

_____

Program your mind daily! As soon as one affirmation is complete or the goal has been reached, create another. Make affirmations a daily habit and soon you will not feel right unless you have done your daily practice. This will keep you focused in the direction of your dreams. Feel free to experiment with different oils as you progress.

Date of Personal AFT Session: _____

Step 1 - Set Your Intention: _____
_____

Rating your intention. How possible does it feel? (Circle One)

    Zero Hope - 0 1 2 3 4 5 6 7 8 9 10 - Absolute Confidence

Step 2 - What does the negative voice say that tells you this is not possible? _____
_____

Step 3 - How do you feel when you hear this negative voice (find ONE word)? _____

Step 4 - Where do you feel this in your body? _____

Step 5 - Drift back to an earlier time when you felt the same way - get a snapshot or a movie. (Circle One)

    Snapshot   Movie   No Image

Notes on previous memory _____
_____

Step 6 - Smell Memory Release Blend or other oils - specify which oils used: _____

Step 7 - Notice changes: _____
_____

Step 8 - Is there a new belief or mindset that has emerged? _____
_____

Step 9 - Read the original intention and rate it again - how possible does it feel now? (circle one)

    Zero Hope - 0 1 2 3 4 5 6 7 8 9 10 - Absolute Confidence

(If 8 or higher (or if no negative voice), skip to Step 10 - the Affirmation. If less than 8, return to Step 2 on next page.)

How far have you shifted thus far?

Starting number: _____ New Number: _____

Step 2 - Re-read the intention and listen for what else the negative voice says about why it can't happen. _____

_____

Step 3 - How do you feel when you hear the negative voice? (find ONE word) _____

Step 4 - Where do you feel this in your body? _____

_____

Step 5 - Drift back to an earlier time when you felt the same way - get a snapshot or a movie. (Circle One)

Snapshot   Movie   No Image

Notes on previous memory: _____

_____

Step 6 - Smell Memory Release Blend or other oils - specify which oils used: _____

Step 7 - Notice changes _____

_____

Step 8 - Is there a new belief or mindset that has emerged? _____

_____

Step 9 - Read the original intention and rate it again - how possible does it feel now? (circle)

Zero Hope - 0 1 2 3 4 5 6 7 8 9 10 - Absolute Confidence

Look how far you've shifted!

Starting number: _____ Second Number: _____

Final Number: _____

(Move forward to Step 10 - the Affirmation - even if you're not yet at an 8 or higher. More shifting will occur during the next 3 steps.)

Step 10 - Affirmation: _____

_____

_____

_____

Step 11 - Stand in Power Pose: Repeat the affirmation for 2 minutes, twice daily, with conviction while standing in a power pose. Smell *Believe*™ or *Transformation*™ Oil Blend as you do this. (You may choose another transforming oil if you'd like, such as *Build Your Dream*™, *Magnify Your Purpose*™, etc)

Repeat for _at least three consecutive days_, or until you create a new affirmation. Check off each box when complete.

Always make sure that your energy feels clear when you say the statement. If you experience inner resistance, use the AFT process to identify and release any negative thoughts, feelings, or memories that come up.

Date	AM	PM

Step 12 - Make Your Plan of Action: _____

_____

_____

_____

_____

139

Follow-up - What has changed in your life because of THIS Aroma Freedom Technique Session? _____

_____
_____
_____
_____
_____
_____
_____
_____
_____
_____
_____
_____
_____
_____
_____
_____
_____
_____
_____
_____

Program your mind daily! As soon as one affirmation is complete or the goal has been reached, create another. Make affirmations a daily habit and soon you will not feel right unless you have done your daily practice. This will keep you focused in the direction of your dreams. Feel free to experiment with different oils as you progress.

Date of Personal AFT Session: _____

Step 1 - Set Your Intention: _____
_____

Rating your intention. How possible does it feel? (Circle One)

    Zero Hope - 0 1 2 3 4 5 6 7 8 9 10 - Absolute Confidence

Step 2 - What does the negative voice say that tells you this is not possible? _____

Step 3 - How do you feel when you hear this negative voice (find ONE word)? _____

Step 4 - Where do you feel this in your body? _____

Step 5 - Drift back to an earlier time when you felt the same way - get a snapshot or a movie. (Circle One)

       Snapshot   Movie   No Image

Notes on previous memory _____
_____

Step 6 - Smell Memory Release Blend or other oils - specify which oils used: _____

Step 7 - Notice changes: _____
_____

Step 8 - Is there a new belief or mindset that has emerged? _____
_____

Step 9 - Read the original intention and rate it again - how possible does it feel now? (circle one)

    Zero Hope - 0 1 2 3 4 5 6 7 8 9 10 - Absolute Confidence

(If 8 or higher (or if no negative voice), skip to Step 10 - the Affirmation. If less than 8, return to Step 2 on next page.)

How far have you shifted thus far?

Starting number: _____ New Number: _____

Step 2 - Re-read the intention and listen for what else the negative voice says about why it can't happen. _____

_____

Step 3 - How do you feel when you hear the negative voice? (find ONE word) _____

Step 4 - Where do you feel this in your body? _____

_____

Step 5 - Drift back to an earlier time when you felt the same way - get a snapshot or a movie. (Circle One)

Snapshot   Movie   No Image

Notes on previous memory: _____

_____

Step 6 - Smell Memory Release Blend or other oils - specify which oils used: _____

Step 7 - Notice changes _____

_____

Step 8 - Is there a new belief or mindset that has emerged? _____

_____

Step 9 - Read the original intention and rate it again - how possible does it feel now? (circle)

Zero Hope - 0 1 2 3 4 5 6 7 8 9 10 - Absolute Confidence

Look how far you've shifted!

Starting number: _____ Second Number: _____

Final Number: _____

(Move forward to Step 10 - the Affirmation - even if you're not yet at an 8 or higher. More shifting will occur during the next 3 steps.)

Step 10 - Affirmation: _____

_____

_____
_____
_____

Step 11 - Stand in Power Pose: Repeat the affirmation for 2 minutes, twice daily, with conviction while standing in a power pose, Smell *Believe*™ or *Transformation*™ Oil Blend as you do this. (You may choose another transforming oil if you'd like, such as *Build Your Dream*™, *Magnify Your Purpose*™, etc)

Repeat for *at least three consecutive days,* or until you create a new affirmation. Check off each box when complete.

Always make sure that your energy feels clear when you say the statement. If you experience inner resistance, use the AFT process to identify and release any negative thoughts, feelings, or memories that come up.

Date	AM	PM

Step 12 - Make Your Plan of Action: _____

_____
_____
_____
_____
_____
_____

Follow-up - What has changed in your life because of THIS Aroma Freedom Technique Session? _____

_____

_____

_____

_____

_____

_____

_____

_____

_____

_____

_____

_____

_____

_____

_____

_____

_____

_____

Program your mind daily! As soon as one affirmation is complete or the goal has been reached, create another. Make affirmations a daily habit and soon you will not feel right unless you have done your daily practice. This will keep you focused in the direction of your dreams. Feel free to experiment with different oils as you progress.

Date of Personal AFT Session: _____

Step 1 - Set Your Intention: _____
_____

Rating your intention. How possible does it feel? (Circle One)

    Zero Hope - 0 1 2 3 4 5 6 7 8 9 10 - Absolute Confidence

Step 2 - What does the negative voice say that tells you this is not possible? _____

Step 3 - How do you feel when you hear this negative voice (find ONE word)? _____

Step 4 - Where do you feel this in your body? _____

Step 5 - Drift back to an earlier time when you felt the same way - get a snapshot or a movie. (Circle One)

    Snapshot   Movie   No Image

Notes on previous memory _____
_____

Step 6 - Smell Memory Release Blend or other oils - specify which oils used: _____

Step 7 - Notice changes: _____
_____

Step 8 - Is there a new belief or mindset that has emerged? _____
_____

Step 9 - Read the original intention and rate it again - how possible does it feel now? (circle one)

    Zero Hope - 0 1 2 3 4 5 6 7 8 9 10 - Absolute Confidence

(If 8 or higher (or if no negative voice), skip to Step 10 - the Affirmation. If less than 8, return to Step 2 on next page.)

How far have you shifted thus far?

Starting number: _____ New Number: _____

Step 2 - Re-read the intention and listen for what else the negative voice says about why it can't happen. _____

_____

Step 3 - How do you feel when you hear the negative voice? (find ONE word) _____

Step 4 - Where do you feel this in your body? _____

_____

_____

Step 5 - Drift back to an earlier time when you felt the same way - get a snapshot or a movie. (Circle One)

Snapshot   Movie   No Image

Notes on previous memory: _____

_____

_____

Step 6 - Smell Memory Release Blend or other oils - specify which oils used: _____

Step 7 - Notice changes _____

_____

_____

Step 8 - Is there a new belief or mindset that has emerged? _____

_____

_____

Step 9 - Read the original intention and rate it again - how possible does it feel now? (circle)

Zero Hope - 0 1 2 3 4 5 6 7 8 9 10 - Absolute Confidence

Look how far you've shifted!

Starting number: _____ Second Number: _____

Final Number: _____

(Move forward to Step 10 - the Affirmation - even if you're not yet at an 8 or higher. More shifting will occur during the next 3 steps.)

Step 10 - Affirmation: _____

_____

_____

_____

Step 11 - Stand in Power Pose: Repeat the affirmation for 2 minutes, twice daily, with conviction while standing in a power pose. Smell *Believe*™ or *Transformation*™ Oil Blend as you do this. (You may choose another transforming oil if you'd like, such as *Build Your Dream*™, *Magnify Your Purpose*™, etc)

Repeat for _at least three consecutive days_, or until you create a new affirmation. Check off each box when complete.

Always make sure that your energy feels clear when you say the statement. If you experience inner resistance, use the AFT process to identify and release any negative thoughts, feelings, or memories that come up.

Date	AM	PM

Step 12 - Make Your Plan of Action: _____

_____

_____

_____

_____

_____

Follow-up - What has changed in your life because of THIS Aroma Freedom Technique Session? _____

_____

_____

_____

_____

_____

_____

_____

_____

_____

_____

_____

_____

_____

_____

_____

_____

_____

_____

_____

_____

Program your mind daily! As soon as one affirmation is complete or the goal has been reached, create another. Make affirmations a daily habit and soon you will not feel right unless you have done your daily practice. This will keep you focused in the direction of your dreams. Feel free to experiment with different oils as you progress.

Date of Personal AFT Session: _____

Step 1 - Set Your Intention: _____
_____

Rating your intention. How possible does it feel? (Circle One)

     Zero Hope - 0 1 2 3 4 5 6 7 8 9 10 - Absolute Confidence

Step 2 - What does the negative voice say that tells you this is not possible? _____

Step 3 - How do you feel when you hear this negative voice (find ONE word)? _____

Step 4 - Where do you feel this in your body? _____

Step 5 - Drift back to an earlier time when you felt the same way - get a snapshot or a movie. (Circle One)

     Snapshot   Movie   No Image

Notes on previous memory _____
_____

Step 6 - Smell Memory Release Blend or other oils - specify which oils used: _____

Step 7 - Notice changes: _____
_____

Step 8 - Is there a new belief or mindset that has emerged? _____
_____

Step 9 - Read the original intention and rate it again - how possible does it feel now? (circle one)

     Zero Hope - 0 1 2 3 4 5 6 7 8 9 10 - Absolute Confidence

(If 8 or higher (or if no negative voice), skip to Step 10 - the Affirmation. If less than 8, return to Step 2 on next page.)

How far have you shifted thus far?

Starting number: _____ New Number: _____

Step 2 - Re-read the intention and listen for what else the negative voice says about why it can't happen. _____

_____

Step 3 - How do you feel when you hear the negative voice? (find ONE word) _____

Step 4 - Where do you feel this in your body? _____

_____

Step 5 - Drift back to an earlier time when you felt the same way - get a snapshot or a movie. (Circle One)

Snapshot   Movie   No Image

Notes on previous memory: _____

_____

Step 6 - Smell Memory Release Blend or other oils - specify which oils used: _____

Step 7 - Notice changes _____

_____

Step 8 - Is there a new belief or mindset that has emerged? _____

_____

Step 9 - Read the original intention and rate it again - how possible does it feel now? (circle)

Zero Hope - 0 1 2 3 4 5 6 7 8 9 10 - Absolute Confidence

Look how far you've shifted!

Starting number: _____ Second Number: _____

Final Number: _____

(Move forward to Step 10 - the Affirmation - even if you're not yet at an 8 or higher. More shifting will occur during the next 3 steps.)

Step 10 - Affirmation: _____

_____
_____
_____

Step 11 - Stand in Power Pose: Repeat the affirmation for 2 minutes, twice daily, with conviction while standing in a power pose. Smell *Believe*™ or *Transformation*™ Oil Blend as you do this. (You may choose another transforming oil if you'd like, such as *Build Your Dream*™, *Magnify Your Purpose*™, etc)

Repeat for *at least three consecutive days*, or until you create a new affirmation. Check off each box when complete.

Always make sure that your energy feels clear when you say the statement. If you experience inner resistance, use the AFT process to identify and release any negative thoughts, feelings, or memories that come up.

Date	AM	PM

Step 12 - Make Your Plan of Action: _____

_____
_____
_____
_____
_____

Follow-up - What has changed in your life because of THIS Aroma Freedom Technique Session? _____

_____

_____

_____

_____

_____

_____

_____

_____

_____

_____

_____

_____

_____

_____

_____

_____

_____

_____

Program your mind daily! As soon as one affirmation is complete or the goal has been reached, create another. Make affirmations a daily habit and soon you will not feel right unless you have done your daily practice. This will keep you focused in the direction of your dreams. Feel free to experiment with different oils as you progress.

Date of Personal AFT Session: _____

Step 1 - Set Your Intention: _____
_____

Rating your intention. How possible does it feel? (Circle One)

    Zero Hope   0 1 2 3 4 5 6 7 8 9 10 - Absolute Confidence

Step 2 - What does the negative voice say that tells you this is not possible? _____

Step 3 - How do you feel when you hear this negative voice (find ONE word)? _____

Step 4 - Where do you feel this in your body? _____

Step 5 - Drift back to an earlier time when you felt the same way - get a snapshot or a movie. (Circle One)

    Snapshot   Movie   No Image

Notes on previous memory _____
_____

Step 6 - Smell Memory Release Blend or other oils - specify which oils used: _____

Step 7 - Notice changes: _____
_____

Step 8 - Is there a new belief or mindset that has emerged? _____
_____

Step 9 - Read the original intention and rate it again - how possible does it feel now? (circle one)

    Zero Hope - 0 1 2 3 4 5 6 7 8 9 10 - Absolute Confidence

(If 8 or higher (or if no negative voice), skip to Step 10 - the Affirmation. If less than 8, return to Step 2 on next page.)

How far have you shifted thus far?

        Starting number: _____ New Number: _____

Step 2 - Re-read the intention and listen for what else the negative voice says about why it can't happen. _____

_____

Step 3 - How do you feel when you hear the negative voice? (find ONE word) _____

Step 4 - Where do you feel this in your body? _____

_____

Step 5 - Drift back to an earlier time when you felt the same way - get a snapshot or a movie. (Circle One)

        Snapshot   Movie   No Image

Notes on previous memory: _____

_____

Step 6 - Smell Memory Release Blend or other oils - specify which oils used: _____

Step 7 - Notice changes _____

_____

Step 8 - Is there a new belief or mindset that has emerged? _____

_____

Step 9 - Read the original intention and rate it again - how possible does it feel now? (circle)

     Zero Hope - 0 1 2 3 4 5 6 7 8 9 10 - Absolute Confidence

Look how far you've shifted!

        Starting number: _____ Second Number: _____

              Final Number: _____

(Move forward to Step 10 - the Affirmation - even if you're not yet at an 8 or higher. More shifting will occur during the next 3 steps.)

Step 10 - Affirmation: _____

_____

_____

_____

Step 11 - Stand in Power Pose: Repeat the affirmation for 2 minutes, twice daily, with conviction while standing in a power pose. Smell *Believe*™ or *Transformation*™ Oil Blend as you do this. (You may choose another transforming oil if you'd like, such as *Build Your Dream*™, *Magnify Your Purpose*™, etc)

Repeat for *at least three consecutive days*, or until you create a new affirmation. Check off each box when complete.

Always make sure that your energy feels clear when you say the statement. If you experience inner resistance, use the AFT process to identify and release any negative thoughts, feelings, or memories that come up.

Date	AM	PM

Step 12 - Make Your Plan of Action: _____

_____

_____

_____

_____

_____

Follow-up - What has changed in your life because of THIS Aroma Freedom Technique Session? _____

_____
_____
_____
_____
_____
_____
_____
_____
_____
_____
_____
_____
_____
_____
_____
_____
_____
_____
_____
_____

Program your mind daily! As soon as one affirmation is complete or the goal has been reached, create another. Make affirmations a daily habit and soon you will not feel right unless you have done your daily practice. This will keep you focused in the direction of your dreams. Feel free to experiment with different oils as you progress.

Date of Personal AFT Session: _____

Step 1 - Set Your Intention: _____
_____
_____

Rating your intention. How possible does it feel? (Circle One)

    Zero Hope - 0 1 2 3 4 5 6 7 8 9 10 - Absolute Confidence

Step 2 - What does the negative voice say that tells you this is not possible? _____
_____

Step 3 - How do you feel when you hear this negative voice (find ONE word)? _____

Step 4 - Where do you feel this in your body? _____

Step 5 - Drift back to an earlier time when you felt the same way - get a snapshot or a movie. (Circle One)

    Snapshot   Movie   No Image

Notes on previous memory _____
_____
_____

Step 6 - Smell Memory Release Blend or other oils - specify which oils used: _____

Step 7 - Notice changes: _____
_____
_____

Step 8 - Is there a new belief or mindset that has emerged? _____
_____
_____

Step 9 - Read the original intention and rate it again - how possible does it feel now? (circle one)

    Zero Hope - 0 1 2 3 4 5 6 7 8 9 10 - Absolute Confidence

(If 8 or higher (or if no negative voice), skip to Step 10 - the Affirmation. If less than 8, return to Step 2 on next page.)

How far have you shifted thus far?

　　　　Starting number: _____ New Number: _____

Step 2 - Re-read the intention and listen for what else the negative voice says about why it can't happen. _____

_____

Step 3 - How do you feel when you hear the negative voice? (find ONE word) _____

Step 4 - Where do you feel this in your body? _____

_____

Step 5 - Drift back to an earlier time when you felt the same way - get a snapshot or a movie. (Circle One)

　　　　Snapshot　　　Movie　　　No Image

Notes on previous memory: _____

_____

Step 6 - Smell Memory Release Blend or other oils - specify which oils used: _____

Step 7 - Notice changes _____

_____

Step 8 - Is there a new belief or mindset that has emerged? _____

_____

Step 9 - Read the original intention and rate it again - how possible does it feel now? (circle)

　　　　Zero Hope - 0　1　2　3　4　5　6　7　8　9　10 - Absolute Confidence

Look how far you've shifted!

　　　　Starting number: _____ Second Number: _____

　　　　　　　　Final Number: _____

(Move forward to Step 10 - the Affirmation - even if you're not yet at an 8 or higher. More shifting will occur during the next 3 steps.)

Step 10 - Affirmation: _____

_____

_____
_____

Step 11 - Stand in Power Pose: Repeat the affirmation for 2 minutes, twice daily, with conviction while standing in a power pose. Smell *Believe*™ or *Transformation*™ Oil Blend as you do this. (You may choose another transforming oil if you'd like, such as *Build Your Dream*™, *Magnify Your Purpose*™, etc)

Repeat for <u>*at least three consecutive days,*</u> or until you create a new affirmation. Check off each box when complete.

Always make sure that your energy feels clear when you say the statement. If you experience inner resistance, use the AFT process to identify and release any negative thoughts, feelings, or memories that come up.

Date	AM	PM

Step 12 - Make Your Plan of Action: _____

_____
_____
_____
_____
_____

Follow-up - What has changed in your life because of THIS Aroma Freedom Technique Session? _____

_____
_____
_____
_____
_____
_____
_____
_____
_____
_____
_____
_____
_____
_____
_____
_____
_____
_____
_____
_____

Program your mind daily! As soon as one affirmation is complete or the goal has been reached, create another. Make affirmations a daily habit and soon you will not feel right unless you have done your daily practice. This will keep you focused in the direction of your dreams. Feel free to experiment with different oils as you progress.

Date of Personal AFT Session: _____

Step 1 - Set Your Intention: _____

_____

Rating your intention. How possible does it feel? (Circle One)

    Zero Hope - 0 1 2 3 4 5 6 7 8 9 10 - Absolute Confidence

Step 2 - What does the negative voice say that tells you this is not possible? _____

_____

Step 3 - How do you feel when you hear this negative voice (find ONE word)? _____

Step 4 - Where do you feel this in your body? _____

_____

Step 5 - Drift back to an earlier time when you felt the same way - get a snapshot or a movie. (Circle One)

    Snapshot   Movie   No Image

Notes on previous memory _____

_____

Step 6 - Smell Memory Release Blend or other oils - specify which oils used: _____

Step 7 - Notice changes: _____

_____

Step 8 - Is there a new belief or mindset that has emerged? _____

_____

Step 9 - Read the original intention and rate it again - how possible does it feel now? (circle one)

    Zero Hope - 0 1 2 3 4 5 6 7 8 9 10 - Absolute Confidence

(If 8 or higher (or if no negative voice), skip to Step 10 - the Affirmation. If less than 8, return to Step 2 on next page.)

How far have you shifted thus far?

      Starting number: _____ New Number: _____

Step 2 - Re-read the intention and listen for what else the negative voice says about why it can't happen. _____

_____

Step 3 - How do you feel when you hear the negative voice? (find ONE word) _____

Step 4 - Where do you feel this in your body? _____

_____

Step 5 - Drift back to an earlier time when you felt the same way - get a snapshot or a movie. (Circle One)

        Snapshot   Movie   No Image

Notes on previous memory: _____

_____

Step 6 - Smell Memory Release Blend or other oils - specify which oils used: _____

Step 7 - Notice changes _____

_____

Step 8 - Is there a new belief or mindset that has emerged? _____

_____

Step 9 - Read the original intention and rate it again - how possible does it feel now? (circle)

      Zero Hope - 0 1 2 3 4 5 6 7 8 9 10 - Absolute Confidence

Look how far you've shifted!

      Starting number: _____ Second Number: _____

          Final Number: _____

(Move forward to Step 10 - the Affirmation - even if you're not yet at an 8 or higher. More shifting will occur during the next 3 steps.)

Step 10 - Affirmation: _____

_____

_____

_____

Step 11 - Stand in Power Pose: Repeat the affirmation for 2 minutes, twice daily, with conviction while standing in a power pose. Smell *Believe*™ or *Transformation*™ Oil Blend as you do this. (You may choose another transforming oil if you'd like, such as *Build Your Dream*™, *Magnify Your Purpose*™, etc)

Repeat for *at least three consecutive days*, or until you create a new affirmation. Check off each box when complete.

Always make sure that your energy feels clear when you say the statement. If you experience inner resistance, use the AFT process to identify and release any negative thoughts, feelings, or memories that come up.

Date	AM	PM

Step 12 - Make Your Plan of Action: _____

_____

_____

_____

_____

_____

Follow-up - What has changed in your life because of THIS Aroma Freedom Technique Session? _____

_____
_____
_____
_____
_____
_____
_____
_____
_____
_____
_____
_____
_____
_____
_____
_____
_____
_____
_____

Program your mind daily! As soon as one affirmation is complete or the goal has been reached, create another. Make affirmations a daily habit and soon you will not feel right unless you have done your daily practice. This will keep you focused in the direction of your dreams. Feel free to experiment with different oils as you progress.

Date of Personal AFT Session: _____

Step 1 - Set Your Intention: _____

_____

Rating your intention. How possible does it feel? (Circle One)

   Zero Hope - 0 1 2 3 4 5 6 7 8 9 10 - Absolute Confidence

Step 2 - What does the negative voice say that tells you this is not possible? _____

Step 3 - How do you feel when you hear this negative voice (find ONE word)? _____

Step 4 - Where do you feel this in your body? _____

Step 5 - Drift back to an earlier time when you felt the same way - get a snapshot or a movie. (Circle One)

   Snapshot   Movie   No Image

Notes on previous memory _____

_____

Step 6 - Smell Memory Release Blend or other oils - specify which oils used: _____

Step 7 - Notice changes: _____

_____

Step 8 - Is there a new belief or mindset that has emerged? _____

_____

Step 9 - Read the original intention and rate it again - how possible does it feel now? (circle one)

   Zero Hope - 0 1 2 3 4 5 6 7 8 9 10 - Absolute Confidence

(If 8 or higher (or if no negative voice), skip to Step 10 - the Affirmation. If less than 8, return to Step 2 on next page.)

How far have you shifted thus far?

Starting number: _____ New Number: _____

Step 2 - Re-read the intention and listen for what else the negative voice says about why it can't happen. _____

_____

Step 3 - How do you feel when you hear the negative voice? (find ONE word) _____

Step 4 - Where do you feel this in your body? _____

_____

Step 5 - Drift back to an earlier time when you felt the same way - get a snapshot or a movie. (Circle One)

Snapshot   Movie   No Image

Notes on previous memory: _____

_____

Step 6 - Smell Memory Release Blend or other oils - specify which oils used: _____

Step 7 - Notice changes _____

_____

Step 8 - Is there a new belief or mindset that has emerged? _____

_____

Step 9 - Read the original intention and rate it again - how possible does it feel now? (circle)

Zero Hope - 0 1 2 3 4 5 6 7 8 9 10 - Absolute Confidence

Look how far you've shifted!

Starting number: _____ Second Number: _____

Final Number: _____

(Move forward to Step 10 - the Affirmation - even if you're not yet at an 8 or higher. More shifting will occur during the next 3 steps.)

Step 10 - Affirmation: _____

_____

_____

_____

Step 11 - Stand in Power Pose: Repeat the affirmation for 2 minutes, twice daily, with conviction while standing in a power pose. Smell *Believe*™ or *Transformation*™ Oil Blend as you do this. (You may choose another transforming oil if you'd like, such as *Build Your Dream*™, *Magnify Your Purpose*™, etc)

Repeat for *at least three consecutive days*, or until you create a new affirmation. Check off each box when complete.

Always make sure that your energy feels clear when you say the statement. If you experience inner resistance, use the AFT process to identify and release any negative thoughts, feelings, or memories that come up.

Date	AM	PM

Step 12 - Make Your Plan of Action: _____

_____

_____

_____

_____

_____

Follow-up - What has changed in your life because of THIS Aroma Freedom Technique Session? _____

_____

_____

_____

_____

_____

_____

_____

_____

_____

_____

_____

_____

_____

_____

_____

_____

_____

_____

_____

_____

_____

Program your mind daily! As soon as one affirmation is complete or the goal has been reached, create another. Make affirmations a daily habit and soon you will not feel right unless you have done your daily practice. This will keep you focused in the direction of your dreams. Feel free to experiment with different oils as you progress.

Date of Personal AFT Session: _____

Step 1 - Set Your Intention: _____
_____

Rating your intention. How possible does it feel? (Circle One)

    Zero Hope - 0 1 2 3 4 5 6 7 8 9 10 - Absolute Confidence

Step 2 - What does the negative voice say that tells you this is not possible? _____

Step 3 - How do you feel when you hear this negative voice (find ONE word)? _____
Step 4 - Where do you feel this in your body? _____

Step 5 - Drift back to an earlier time when you felt the same way - get a snapshot or a movie. (Circle One)

    Snapshot   Movie   No Image

Notes on previous memory _____
_____

Step 6 - Smell Memory Release Blend or other oils - specify which oils used: _____
Step 7 - Notice changes: _____
_____

Step 8 - Is there a new belief or mindset that has emerged? _____
_____

Step 9 - Read the original intention and rate it again - how possible does it feel now? (circle one)

    Zero Hope - 0 1 2 3 4 5 6 7 8 9 10 - Absolute Confidence

(If 8 or higher (or if no negative voice), skip to Step 10 - the Affirmation. If less than 8, return to Step 2 on next page.)

How far have you shifted thus far?

        Starting number: _____ New Number: _____

Step 2 - Re-read the intention and listen for what else the negative voice says about why it can't happen. _____

_____

Step 3 - How do you feel when you hear the negative voice? (find ONE word) _____

Step 4 - Where do you feel this in your body? _____

_____

Step 5 - Drift back to an earlier time when you felt the same way - get a snapshot or a movie. (Circle One)

        Snapshot   Movie   No Image

Notes on previous memory: _____

_____

Step 6 - Smell Memory Release Blend or other oils - specify which oils used: _____

Step 7 - Notice changes _____

_____

Step 8 - Is there a new belief or mindset that has emerged? _____

_____

Step 9 - Read the original intention and rate it again - how possible does it feel now? (circle)

      Zero Hope - 0 1 2 3 4 5 6 7 8 9 10 - Absolute Confidence

Look how far you've shifted!

        Starting number: _____ Second Number: _____
               Final Number: _____

(Move forward to Step 10 - the Affirmation - even if you're not yet at an 8 or higher. More shifting will occur during the next 3 steps.)

Step 10 - Affirmation: _____

_____

_____

_____

Step 11 - Stand in Power Pose: Repeat the affirmation for 2 minutes, twice daily, with conviction while standing in a power pose. Smell _Believe™_ or _Transformation™_ Oil Blend as you do this. (You may choose another transforming oil if you'd like, such as _Build Your Dream™_, _Magnify Your Purpose™_, etc)

Repeat for _at least three consecutive days_, or until you create a new affirmation. Check off each box when complete.

Always make sure that your energy feels clear when you say the statement. If you experience inner resistance, use the AFT process to identify and release any negative thoughts, feelings, or memories that come up.

Date	AM	PM

Step 12 - Make Your Plan of Action: _____

_____

_____

_____

_____

_____

Follow-up - What has changed in your life because of THIS Aroma Freedom Technique Session? _____

_____

_____

_____

_____

_____

_____

_____

_____

_____

_____

_____

_____

_____

_____

_____

_____

_____

_____

_____

_____

Program your mind daily! As soon as one affirmation is complete or the goal has been reached, create another. Make affirmations a daily habit and soon you will not feel right unless you have done your daily practice. This will keep you focused in the direction of your dreams. Feel free to experiment with different oils as you progress.

Date of Personal AFT Session: _____

Step 1 - Set Your Intention: _____
_____
_____

Rating your intention. How possible does it feel? (Circle One)

Zero Hope - 0 1 2 3 4 5 6 7 8 9 10 - Absolute Confidence

Step 2 - What does the negative voice say that tells you this is not possible? _____
_____

Step 3 - How do you feel when you hear this negative voice (find ONE word)? _____

Step 4 - Where do you feel this in your body? _____
_____

Step 5 - Drift back to an earlier time when you felt the same way - get a snapshot or a movie. (Circle One)

Snapshot   Movie   No Image

Notes on previous memory _____
_____
_____

Step 6 - Smell Memory Release Blend or other oils - specify which oils used: _____

Step 7 - Notice changes: _____
_____
_____

Step 8 - Is there a new belief or mindset that has emerged? _____
_____
_____

Step 9 - Read the original intention and rate it again - how possible does it feel now? (circle one)

Zero Hope - 0 1 2 3 4 5 6 7 8 9 10 - Absolute Confidence

(If 8 or higher (or if no negative voice), skip to Step 10 - the Affirmation. If less than 8, return to Step 2 on next page.)

173

How far have you shifted thus far?

Starting number: _____ New Number: _____

Step 2 - Re-read the intention and listen for what else the negative voice says about why it can't happen. _____

_____

Step 3 - How do you feel when you hear the negative voice? (find ONE word) _____

Step 4 - Where do you feel this in your body? _____

_____

Step 5 - Drift back to an earlier time when you felt the same way - get a snapshot or a movie. (Circle One)

Snapshot   Movie   No Image

Notes on previous memory: _____

_____

Step 6 - Smell Memory Release Blend or other oils - specify which oils used: _____

Step 7 - Notice changes _____

_____

Step 8 - Is there a new belief or mindset that has emerged? _____

_____

Step 9 - Read the original intention and rate it again - how possible does it feel now? (circle)

Zero Hope - 0 1 2 3 4 5 6 7 8 9 10 - Absolute Confidence

Look how far you've shifted!

Starting number: _____ Second Number: _____

Final Number: _____

(Move forward to Step 10 - the Affirmation - even if you're not yet at an 8 or higher. More shifting will occur during the next 3 steps.)

Step 10 - Affirmation: _____

_____

_____

_____

Step 11 - Stand in Power Pose: Repeat the affirmation for 2 minutes, twice daily, with conviction while standing in a power pose. Smell *Believe*™ or *Transformation*™ Oil Blend as you do this. (You may choose another transforming oil if you'd like, such as *Build Your Dream*™, *Magnify Your Purpose*™, etc)

Repeat for <u>*at least three consecutive days,*</u> or until you create a new affirmation. Check off each box when complete.

Always make sure that your energy feels clear when you say the statement. If you experience inner resistance, use the AFT process to identify and release any negative thoughts, feelings, or memories that come up.

Date	AM	PM

Step 12 - Make Your Plan of Action: _____

_____

_____

_____

_____

_____

_____

Follow-up - What has changed in your life because of THIS Aroma Freedom Technique Session? _____

_____
_____
_____
_____
_____
_____
_____
_____
_____
_____
_____
_____
_____
_____
_____
_____
_____
_____
_____
_____

Program your mind daily! As soon as one affirmation is complete or the goal has been reached, create another. Make affirmations a daily habit and soon you will not feel right unless you have done your daily practice. This will keep you focused in the direction of your dreams. Feel free to experiment with different oils as you progress.

Date of Personal AFT Session: _____

Step 1 - Set Your Intention: _____
_____
_____

Rating your intention. How possible does it feel? (Circle One)

    Zero Hope - 0 1 2 3 4 5 6 7 8 9 10 - Absolute Confidence

Step 2 - What does the negative voice say that tells you this is not possible? _____
_____

Step 3 - How do you feel when you hear this negative voice (find ONE word)? _____

Step 4 - Where do you feel this in your body? _____
_____

Step 5 - Drift back to an earlier time when you felt the same way - get a snapshot or a movie. (Circle One)

    Snapshot   Movie   No Image

Notes on previous memory _____
_____
_____

Step 6 - Smell Memory Release Blend or other oils - specify which oils used: _____

Step 7 - Notice changes: _____
_____
_____

Step 8 - Is there a new belief or mindset that has emerged? _____
_____
_____

Step 9 - Read the original intention and rate it again - how possible does it feel now? (circle one)

    Zero Hope - 0 1 2 3 4 5 6 7 8 9 10 - Absolute Confidence

(If 8 or higher (or if no negative voice), skip to Step 10 - the Affirmation. If less than 8, return to Step 2 on next page.)

How far have you shifted thus far?

        Starting number: _____ New Number: _____

Step 2 - Re-read the intention and listen for what else the negative voice says about why it can't happen. _____

_____

Step 3 - How do you feel when you hear the negative voice? (find ONE word) _____

Step 4 - Where do you feel this in your body? _____

_____

Step 5 - Drift back to an earlier time when you felt the same way - get a snapshot or a movie. (Circle One)

        Snapshot   Movie   No Image

Notes on previous memory: _____

_____

Step 6 - Smell Memory Release Blend or other oils - specify which oils used: _____

Step 7 - Notice changes _____

_____

Step 8 - Is there a new belief or mindset that has emerged? _____

_____

Step 9 - Read the original intention and rate it again - how possible does it feel now? (circle)

    Zero Hope - 0 1 2 3 4 5 6 7 8 9 10 - Absolute Confidence

Look how far you've shifted!

        Starting number: _____ Second Number: _____

            Final Number: _____

(Move forward to Step 10 - the Affirmation - even if you're not yet at an 8 or higher. More shifting will occur during the next 3 steps.)

178

Step 10 - Affirmation: _____

_____
_____
_____

Step 11 - Stand in Power Pose: Repeat the affirmation for 2 minutes, twice daily, with conviction while standing in a power pose. Smell *Believe*™ or *Transformation*™ Oil Blend as you do this. (You may choose another transforming oil if you'd like, such as *Build Your Dream*™, *Magnify Your Purpose*™, etc)

Repeat for *at least three consecutive days*, or until you create a new affirmation. Check off each box when complete.

Always make sure that your energy feels clear when you say the statement. If you experience inner resistance, use the AFT process to identify and release any negative thoughts, feelings, or memories that come up.

Date	AM	PM

Step 12 - Make Your Plan of Action: _____

_____
_____
_____
_____
_____
_____

Follow-up - What has changed in your life because of THIS Aroma Freedom Technique Session? _____

_____

_____

_____

_____

_____

_____

_____

_____

_____

_____

_____

_____

_____

_____

_____

_____

_____

_____

Program your mind daily! As soon as one affirmation is complete or the goal has been reached, create another. Make affirmations a daily habit and soon you will not feel right unless you have done your daily practice. This will keep you focused in the direction of your dreams. Feel free to experiment with different oils as you progress.

Date of Personal AFT Session: _____

Step 1 - Set Your Intention: _____
_____

Rating your intention. How possible does it feel? (Circle One)

    Zero Hope - 0 1 2 3 4 5 6 7 8 9 10 - Absolute Confidence

Step 2 - What does the negative voice say that tells you this is not possible? _____
_____

Step 3 - How do you feel when you hear this negative voice (find ONE word)? _____
Step 4 - Where do you feel this in your body? _____

Step 5 - Drift back to an earlier time when you felt the same way - get a snapshot or a movie. (Circle One)

      Snapshot   Movie   No Image

Notes on previous memory _____
_____
_____

Step 6 - Smell Memory Release Blend or other oils - specify which oils used: _____
Step 7 - Notice changes: _____
_____
_____

Step 8 - Is there a new belief or mindset that has emerged? _____
_____
_____

Step 9 - Read the original intention and rate it again - how possible does it feel now? (circle one)

    Zero Hope - 0 1 2 3 4 5 6 7 8 9 10 - Absolute Confidence

(If 8 or higher (or if no negative voice), skip to Step 10 - the Affirmation. If less than 8, return to Step 2 on next page.)

How far have you shifted thus far?

        Starting number: _____ New Number: _____

Step 2 - Re-read the intention and listen for what else the negative voice says about why it can't happen. _____

_____

Step 3 - How do you feel when you hear the negative voice? (find ONE word) _____

Step 4 - Where do you feel this in your body? _____

_____

Step 5 - Drift back to an earlier time when you felt the same way - get a snapshot or a movie. (Circle One)

        Snapshot   Movie   No Image

Notes on previous memory: _____

_____

Step 6 - Smell Memory Release Blend or other oils - specify which oils used: _____

Step 7 - Notice changes _____

_____

Step 8 - Is there a new belief or mindset that has emerged? _____

_____

Step 9 - Read the original intention and rate it again - how possible does it feel now? (circle)

       Zero Hope - 0 1 2 3 4 5 6 7 8 9 10 - Absolute Confidence

Look how far you've shifted!

        Starting number: _____ Second Number: _____

             Final Number: _____

(Move forward to Step 10 - the Affirmation - even if you're not yet at an 8 or higher. More shifting will occur during the next 3 steps.)

Step 10 - Affirmation: _____

_____
_____
_____

Step 11 - Stand in Power Pose: Repeat the affirmation for 2 minutes, twice daily, with conviction while standing in a power pose. Smell *Believe*™ or *Transformation*™ Oil Blend as you do this. (You may choose another transforming oil if you'd like, such as *Build Your Dream*™, *Magnify Your Purpose*™, etc)

Repeat for *at least three consecutive days*, or until you create a new affirmation. Check off each box when complete.

Always make sure that your energy feels clear when you say the statement. If you experience inner resistance, use the AFT process to identify and release any negative thoughts, feelings, or memories that come up.

Date	AM	PM

Step 12 - Make Your Plan of Action: _____

_____
_____
_____
_____
_____

Follow-up - What has changed in your life because of THIS Aroma Freedom Technique Session? _____

_____

_____

_____

_____

_____

_____

_____

_____

_____

_____

_____

_____

_____

_____

_____

_____

_____

_____

_____

Program your mind daily! As soon as one affirmation is complete or the goal has been reached, create another. Make affirmations a daily habit and soon you will not feel right unless you have done your daily practice. This will keep you focused in the direction of your dreams. Feel free to experiment with different oils as you progress.

Date of Personal AFT Session: _____

Step 1 - Set Your Intention: _____
_____

Rating your intention. How possible does it feel? (Circle One)

     Zero Hope - 0 1 2 3 4 5 6 7 8 9 10 - Absolute Confidence

Step 2 - What does the negative voice say that tells you this is not possible? _____

Step 3 - How do you feel when you hear this negative voice (find ONE word)? _____

Step 4 - Where do you feel this in your body? _____

Step 5 - Drift back to an earlier time when you felt the same way - get a snapshot or a movie. (Circle One)

     Snapshot   Movie   No Image

Notes on previous memory _____
_____

Step 6 - Smell Memory Release Blend or other oils - specify which oils used: _____

Step 7 - Notice changes: _____
_____

Step 8 - Is there a new belief or mindset that has emerged? _____
_____

Step 9 - Read the original intention and rate it again - how possible does it feel now? (circle one)

     Zero Hope - 0 1 2 3 4 5 6 7 8 9 10 - Absolute Confidence

(If 8 or higher (or if no negative voice), skip to Step 10 - the Affirmation. If less than 8, return to Step 2 on next page.)

How far have you shifted thus far?

       Starting number: _____ New Number: _____

Step 2 - Re-read the intention and listen for what else the negative voice says about why it can't happen. _____

_____

Step 3 - How do you feel when you hear the negative voice? (find ONE word) _____

Step 4 - Where do you feel this in your body? _____

_____

Step 5 - Drift back to an earlier time when you felt the same way - get a snapshot or a movie. (Circle One)

       Snapshot   Movie   No Image

Notes on previous memory: _____

_____

Step 6 - Smell Memory Release Blend or other oils - specify which oils used: _____

Step 7 - Notice changes _____

_____

Step 8 - Is there a new belief or mindset that has emerged? _____

_____

Step 9 - Read the original intention and rate it again - how possible does it feel now? (circle)

       Zero Hope - 0 1 2 3 4 5 6 7 8 9 10 - Absolute Confidence

Look how far you've shifted!

       Starting number: _____ Second Number: _____

              Final Number: _____

(Move forward to Step 10 - the Affirmation - even if you're not yet at an 8 or higher. More shifting will occur during the next 3 steps.)

Step 10 - Affirmation: _____

_____

_____

_____

Step 11 - Stand in Power Pose: Repeat the affirmation for 2 minutes, twice daily, with conviction while standing in a power pose. Smell *Believe*™ or *Transformation*™ Oil Blend as you do this. (You may choose another transforming oil if you'd like, such as *Build Your Dream*™, *Magnify Your Purpose*™, etc)

Repeat for <u>*at least three consecutive days*</u>, or until you create a new affirmation. Check off each box when complete.

Always make sure that your energy feels clear when you say the statement. If you experience inner resistance, use the AFT process to identify and release any negative thoughts, feelings, or memories that come up.

Date	AM	PM

Step 12 - Make Your Plan of Action: _____

_____

_____

_____

_____

_____

Follow-up - What has changed in your life because of THIS Aroma Freedom Technique Session? _____

_____

_____

_____

_____

_____

_____

_____

_____

_____

_____

_____

_____

_____

_____

_____

_____

_____

_____

Program your mind daily! As soon as one affirmation is complete or the goal has been reached, create another. Make affirmations a daily habit and soon you will not feel right unless you have done your daily practice. This will keep you focused in the direction of your dreams. Feel free to experiment with different oils as you progress.

Date of Personal AFT Session: _____

Step 1 - Set Your Intention: _____

_____

Rating your intention. How possible does it feel? (Circle One)

    Zero Hope - 0 1 2 3 4 5 6 7 8 9 10 - Absolute Confidence

Step 2 - What does the negative voice say that tells you this is not possible? _____

_____

Step 3 - How do you feel when you hear this negative voice (find ONE word)? _____

Step 4 - Where do you feel this in your body? _____

Step 5 - Drift back to an earlier time when you felt the same way - get a snapshot or a movie. (Circle One)

    Snapshot   Movie   No Image

Notes on previous memory _____

_____

Step 6 - Smell Memory Release Blend or other oils - specify which oils used: _____

Step 7 - Notice changes: _____

_____

Step 8 - Is there a new belief or mindset that has emerged? _____

_____

Step 9 - Read the original intention and rate it again - how possible does it feel now? (circle one)

    Zero Hope - 0 1 2 3 4 5 6 7 8 9 10 - Absolute Confidence

(If 8 or higher (or if no negative voice), skip to Step 10 - the Affirmation. If less than 8, return to Step 2 on next page.)

How far have you shifted thus far?

        Starting number: _____ New Number: _____

Step 2 - Re-read the intention and listen for what else the negative voice says about why it can't happen. _____

_____

Step 3 - How do you feel when you hear the negative voice? (find ONE word) _____

Step 4 - Where do you feel this in your body? _____

_____

_____

Step 5 - Drift back to an earlier time when you felt the same way - get a snapshot or a movie. (Circle One)

        Snapshot   Movie   No Image

Notes on previous memory: _____

_____

Step 6 - Smell Memory Release Blend or other oils - specify which oils used: _____

Step 7 - Notice changes _____

_____

Step 8 - Is there a new belief or mindset that has emerged? _____

_____

Step 9 - Read the original intention and rate it again - how possible does it feel now? (circle)

    Zero Hope - 0 1 2 3 4 5 6 7 8 9 10 - Absolute Confidence

Look how far you've shifted!

        Starting number: _____ Second Number: _____
               Final Number: _____

(Move forward to Step 10 - the Affirmation - even if you're not yet at an 8 or higher. More shifting will occur during the next 3 steps.)

Step 10 - Affirmation: _____

_____

_____

_____

Step 11 - Stand in Power Pose: Repeat the affirmation for 2 minutes, twice daily, with conviction while standing in a power pose. Smell *Believe*™ or *Transformation*™ Oil Blend as you do this. (You may choose another transforming oil if you'd like, such as *Build Your Dream*™, *Magnify Your Purpose*™, etc)

Repeat for _at least three consecutive days,_ or until you create a new affirmation. Check off each box when complete.

Always make sure that your energy feels clear when you say the statement. If you experience inner resistance, use the AFT process to identify and release any negative thoughts, feelings, or memories that come up.

Date	AM	PM

Step 12 - Make Your Plan of Action: _____

_____

_____

_____

_____

_____

Follow-up - What has changed in your life because of THIS Aroma Freedom Technique Session? _____

_____

_____

_____

_____

_____

_____

_____

_____

_____

_____

_____

_____

_____

_____

_____

_____

_____

_____

_____

Program your mind daily! As soon as one affirmation is complete or the goal has been reached, create another. Make affirmations a daily habit and soon you will not feel right unless you have done your daily practice. This will keep you focused in the direction of your dreams. Feel free to experiment with different oils as you progress.

Date of Personal AFT Session: _____

Step 1 - Set Your Intention: _____

_____

Rating your intention. How possible does it feel? (Circle One)

Zero Hope - 0 1 2 3 4 5 6 7 8 9 10 - Absolute Confidence

Step 2 - What does the negative voice say that tells you this is not possible? _____

_____

Step 3 - How do you feel when you hear this negative voice (find ONE word)? _____

Step 4 - Where do you feel this in your body? _____

Step 5 - Drift back to an earlier time when you felt the same way - get a snapshot or a movie. (Circle One)

Snapshot   Movie   No Image

Notes on previous memory _____

_____

Step 6 - Smell Memory Release Blend or other oils - specify which oils used: _____

Step 7 - Notice changes: _____

_____

Step 8 - Is there a new belief or mindset that has emerged? _____

_____

Step 9 - Read the original intention and rate it again - how possible does it feel now? (circle one)

Zero Hope - 0 1 2 3 4 5 6 7 8 9 10 - Absolute Confidence

(If 8 or higher (or if no negative voice), skip to Step 10 - the Affirmation. If less than 8, return to Step 2 on next page.)

How far have you shifted thus far?
Starting number: _____ New Number: _____

Step 2 - Re-read the intention and listen for what else the negative voice says about why it can't happen. _____
_____

Step 3 - How do you feel when you hear the negative voice? (find ONE word) _____

Step 4 - Where do you feel this in your body? _____
_____

Step 5 - Drift back to an earlier time when you felt the same way - get a snapshot or a movie. (Circle One)

Snapshot   Movie   No Image

Notes on previous memory: _____
_____

Step 6 - Smell Memory Release Blend or other oils - specify which oils used: _____
Step 7 - Notice changes _____
_____

Step 8 - Is there a new belief or mindset that has emerged? _____
_____

Step 9 - Read the original intention and rate it again - how possible does it feel now? (circle)

Zero Hope - 0 1 2 3 4 5 6 7 8 9 10 - Absolute Confidence

Look how far you've shifted!
Starting number: _____ Second Number: _____
Final Number: _____

(Move forward to Step 10 - the Affirmation - even if you're not yet at an 8 or higher. More shifting will occur during the next 3 steps.)

Step 10 - Affirmation: _____

_____
_____
_____

Step 11 - Stand in Power Pose: Repeat the affirmation for 2 minutes, twice daily, with conviction while standing in a power pose. Smell *Believe*™ or *Transformation*™ Oil Blend as you do this. (You may choose another transforming oil if you'd like, such as *Build Your Dream*™, *Magnify Your Purpose*™, etc)

Repeat for *at least three consecutive days*, or until you create a new affirmation. Check off each box when complete.

Always make sure that your energy feels clear when you say the statement. If you experience inner resistance, use the AFT process to identify and release any negative thoughts, feelings, or memories that come up.

Date	AM	PM

Step 12 - Make Your Plan of Action: _____

_____
_____
_____
_____
_____
_____

Follow-up - What has changed in your life because of THIS Aroma Freedom Technique Session? _____

_____

_____

_____

_____

_____

_____

_____

_____

_____

_____

_____

_____

_____

_____

_____

_____

_____

_____

Program your mind daily! As soon as one affirmation is complete or the goal has been reached, create another. Make affirmations a daily habit and soon you will not feel right unless you have done your daily practice. This will keep you focused in the direction of your dreams. Feel free to experiment with different oils as you progress.

Date of Personal AFT Session: _____

Step 1 - Set Your Intention: _____

_____

Rating your intention. How possible does it feel? (Circle One)

    Zero Hope - 0 1 2 3 4 5 6 7 8 9 10 - Absolute Confidence

Step 2 - What does the negative voice say that tells you this is not possible? _____

_____

Step 3 - How do you feel when you hear this negative voice (find ONE word)? _____

Step 4 - Where do you feel this in your body? _____

Step 5 - Drift back to an earlier time when you felt the same way - get a snapshot or a movie. (Circle One)

       Snapshot   Movie   No Image

Notes on previous memory _____

_____

Step 6 - Smell Memory Release Blend or other oils - specify which oils used: _____

Step 7 - Notice changes: _____

_____

Step 8 - Is there a new belief or mindset that has emerged? _____

_____

Step 9 - Read the original intention and rate it again - how possible does it feel now? (circle one)

    Zero Hope - 0 1 2 3 4 5 6 7 8 9 10 - Absolute Confidence

(If 8 or higher (or if no negative voice), skip to Step 10 - the Affirmation. If less than 8, return to Step 2 on next page.)

How far have you shifted thus far?

Starting number: _____ New Number: _____

Step 2 - Re-read the intention and listen for what else the negative voice says about why it can't happen. _____

_____

Step 3 - How do you feel when you hear the negative voice? (find ONE word) _____

Step 4 - Where do you feel this in your body? _____

_____

Step 5 - Drift back to an earlier time when you felt the same way - get a snapshot or a movie. (Circle One)

Snapshot   Movie   No Image

Notes on previous memory: _____

_____

Step 6 - Smell Memory Release Blend or other oils - specify which oils used: _____

Step 7 - Notice changes _____

_____

Step 8 - Is there a new belief or mindset that has emerged? _____

_____

Step 9 - Read the original intention and rate it again - how possible does it feel now? (circle)

Zero Hope - 0 1 2 3 4 5 6 7 8 9 10 - Absolute Confidence

Look how far you've shifted!

Starting number: _____ Second Number: _____

Final Number: _____

(Move forward to Step 10 - the Affirmation - even if you're not yet at an 8 or higher. More shifting will occur during the next 3 steps.)

Step 10 - Affirmation: _____

_____
_____
_____

Step 11 - Stand in Power Pose: Repeat the affirmation for 2 minutes, twice daily, with conviction while standing in a power pose. Smell *Believe*™ or *Transformation*™ Oil Blend as you do this. (You may choose another transforming oil if you'd like, such as *Build Your Dream*™, *Magnify Your Purpose*™, etc)

Repeat for _at least three consecutive days,_ or until you create a new affirmation. Check off each box when complete.

Always make sure that your energy feels clear when you say the statement. If you experience inner resistance, use the AFT process to identify and release any negative thoughts, feelings, or memories that come up.

Date	AM	PM

Step 12 - Make Your Plan of Action: _____

_____
_____
_____
_____
_____

Follow-up - What has changed in your life because of THIS Aroma Freedom Technique Session? _____

_____
_____
_____
_____
_____
_____
_____
_____
_____
_____
_____
_____
_____
_____
_____
_____
_____
_____
_____
_____

Program your mind daily! As soon as one affirmation is complete or the goal has been reached, create another. Make affirmations a daily habit and soon you will not feel right unless you have done your daily practice. This will keep you focused in the direction of your dreams. Feel free to experiment with different oils as you progress.

Date of Personal AFT Session: _____

Step 1 - Set Your Intention: _____
_____
_____

Rating your intention. How possible does it feel? (Circle One)

    Zero Hope - 0 1 2 3 4 5 6 7 8 9 10 - Absolute Confidence

Step 2 - What does the negative voice say that tells you this is not possible? _____
_____

Step 3 - How do you feel when you hear this negative voice (find ONE word)? _____

Step 4 - Where do you feel this in your body? _____

Step 5 - Drift back to an earlier time when you felt the same way - get a snapshot or a movie. (Circle One)

      Snapshot   Movie   No Image

Notes on previous memory _____
_____

Step 6 - Smell Memory Release Blend or other oils - specify which oils used: _____

Step 7 - Notice changes: _____
_____

Step 8 - Is there a new belief or mindset that has emerged? _____
_____

Step 9 - Read the original intention and rate it again - how possible does it feel now? (circle one)

    Zero Hope - 0 1 2 3 4 5 6 7 8 9 10 - Absolute Confidence

(If 8 or higher (or if no negative voice), skip to Step 10 - the Affirmation. If less than 8, return to Step 2 on next page.)

How far have you shifted thus far?

Starting number: _____ New Number: _____

Step 2 - Re-read the intention and listen for what else the negative voice says about why it can't happen. _____

_____

Step 3 - How do you feel when you hear the negative voice? (find ONE word) _____

Step 4 - Where do you feel this in your body? _____

_____

_____

Step 5 - Drift back to an earlier time when you felt the same way - get a snapshot or a movie. (Circle One)

Snapshot   Movie   No Image

Notes on previous memory: _____

_____

_____

Step 6 - Smell Memory Release Blend or other oils - specify which oils used: _____

Step 7 - Notice changes _____

_____

_____

Step 8 - Is there a new belief or mindset that has emerged? _____

_____

_____

Step 9 - Read the original intention and rate it again - how possible does it feel now? (circle)

Zero Hope - 0 1 2 3 4 5 6 7 8 9 10 - Absolute Confidence

Look how far you've shifted!

Starting number: _____ Second Number: _____

Final Number: _____

(Move forward to Step 10 - the Affirmation - even if you're not yet at an 8 or higher. More shifting will occur during the next 3 steps.)

Step 10 - Affirmation: _____

_____

_____

_____

Step 11 - Stand in Power Pose: Repeat the affirmation for 2 minutes, twice daily, with conviction while standing in a power pose. Smell _Believe_™ or _Transformation_™ Oil Blend as you do this. (You may choose another transforming oil if you'd like, such as _Build Your Dream_™, _Magnify Your Purpose_™, etc)

Repeat for _at least three consecutive days_, or until you create a new affirmation. Check off each box when complete.

Always make sure that your energy feels clear when you say the statement. If you experience inner resistance, use the AFT process to identify and release any negative thoughts, feelings, or memories that come up.

Date	AM	PM

Step 12 - Make Your Plan of Action: _____

_____

_____

_____

_____

_____

_____

Follow-up - What has changed in your life because of THIS Aroma Freedom Technique Session? _____

_____
_____
_____
_____
_____
_____
_____
_____
_____
_____
_____
_____
_____
_____
_____
_____
_____
_____
_____
_____
_____

Program your mind daily! As soon as one affirmation is complete or the goal has been reached, create another. Make affirmations a daily habit and soon you will not feel right unless you have done your daily practice. This will keep you focused in the direction of your dreams. Feel free to experiment with different oils as you progress.

Date of Personal AFT Session: _____

Step 1 - Set Your Intention: _____

_____

Rating your intention. How possible does it feel? (Circle One)

    Zero Hope - 0 1 2 3 4 5 6 7 8 9 10 - Absolute Confidence

Step 2 - What does the negative voice say that tells you this is not possible? _____

_____

Step 3 - How do you feel when you hear this negative voice (find ONE word)? _____

Step 4 - Where do you feel this in your body? _____

Step 5 - Drift back to an earlier time when you felt the same way - get a snapshot or a movie. (Circle One)

    Snapshot   Movie   No Image

Notes on previous memory _____

_____

Step 6 - Smell Memory Release Blend or other oils - specify which oils used: _____

Step 7 - Notice changes: _____

_____

Step 8 - Is there a new belief or mindset that has emerged? _____

_____

Step 9 - Read the original intention and rate it again - how possible does it feel now? (circle one)

    Zero Hope - 0 1 2 3 4 5 6 7 8 9 10 - Absolute Confidence

(If 8 or higher (or if no negative voice), skip to Step 10 - the Affirmation. If less than 8, return to Step 2 on next page.)

How far have you shifted thus far?

        Starting number: _____ New Number: _____

Step 2 - Re-read the intention and listen for what else the negative voice says about why it can't happen. _____

_____

Step 3 - How do you feel when you hear the negative voice? (find ONE word) _____

Step 4 - Where do you feel this in your body? _____

_____

Step 5 - Drift back to an earlier time when you felt the same way - get a snapshot or a movie. (Circle One)

        Snapshot   Movie   No Image

Notes on previous memory: _____

_____

Step 6 - Smell Memory Release Blend or other oils - specify which oils used: _____

Step 7 - Notice changes _____

_____

Step 8 - Is there a new belief or mindset that has emerged? _____

_____

Step 9 - Read the original intention and rate it again - how possible does it feel now? (circle)

        Zero Hope - 0 1 2 3 4 5 6 7 8 9 10 - Absolute Confidence

Look how far you've shifted!

        Starting number: _____ Second Number: _____

               Final Number: _____

(Move forward to Step 10 - the Affirmation - even if you're not yet at an 8 or higher. More shifting will occur during the next 3 steps.)

Step 10 - Affirmation: _____

_____
_____
_____

Step 11 - Stand in Power Pose: Repeat the affirmation for 2 minutes, twice daily, with conviction while standing in a power pose. Smell *Believe*™ or *Transformation*™ Oil Blend as you do this. (You may choose another transforming oil if you'd like, such as *Build Your Dream*™, *Magnify Your Purpose*™, etc)

Repeat for *at least three consecutive days,* or until you create a new affirmation. Check off each box when complete.

Always make sure that your energy feels clear when you say the statement. If you experience inner resistance, use the AFT process to identify and release any negative thoughts, feelings, or memories that come up.

Date	AM	PM

Step 12 - Make Your Plan of Action: _____

_____
_____
_____
_____
_____

Follow-up - What has changed in your life because of THIS Aroma Freedom Technique Session? _____

_____

_____

_____

_____

_____

_____

_____

_____

_____

_____

_____

_____

_____

_____

_____

_____

_____

_____

_____

Program your mind daily! As soon as one affirmation is complete or the goal has been reached, create another. Make affirmations a daily habit and soon you will not feel right unless you have done your daily practice. This will keep you focused in the direction of your dreams. Feel free to experiment with different oils as you progress.

Date of Personal AFT Session: _____

Step 1 - Set Your Intention: _____

_____

Rating your intention. How possible does it feel? (Circle One)

    Zero Hope - 0 1 2 3 4 5 6 7 8 9 10 - Absolute Confidence

Step 2 - What does the negative voice say that tells you this is not possible? _____

Step 3 - How do you feel when you hear this negative voice (find ONE word)? _____

Step 4 - Where do you feel this in your body? _____

Step 5 - Drift back to an earlier time when you felt the same way - get a snapshot or a movie. (Circle One)

        Snapshot   Movie   No Image

Notes on previous memory _____

_____

Step 6 - Smell Memory Release Blend or other oils - specify which oils used: _____

Step 7 - Notice changes: _____

_____

Step 8 - Is there a new belief or mindset that has emerged? _____

_____

Step 9 - Read the original intention and rate it again - how possible does it feel now? (circle one)

    Zero Hope - 0 1 2 3 4 5 6 7 8 9 10 - Absolute Confidence

(If 8 or higher (or if no negative voice), skip to Step 10 - the Affirmation. If less than 8, return to Step 2 on next page.)

How far have you shifted thus far?

       Starting number: _____ New Number: _____

Step 2 - Re-read the intention and listen for what else the negative voice says about why it can't happen. _____

_____

Step 3 - How do you feel when you hear the negative voice? (find ONE word) _____

Step 4 - Where do you feel this in your body? _____

_____

Step 5 - Drift back to an earlier time when you felt the same way - get a snapshot or a movie. (Circle One)

       Snapshot   Movie   No Image

Notes on previous memory: _____

_____

Step 6 - Smell Memory Release Blend or other oils - specify which oils used: _____

Step 7 - Notice changes _____

_____

Step 8 - Is there a new belief or mindset that has emerged? _____

_____

Step 9 - Read the original intention and rate it again - how possible does it feel now? (circle)

     Zero Hope - 0 1 2 3 4 5 6 7 8 9 10 - Absolute Confidence

Look how far you've shifted!

       Starting number: _____ Second Number: _____
              Final Number: _____

(Move forward to Step 10 - the Affirmation - even if you're not yet at an 8 or higher. More shifting will occur during the next 3 steps.)

Step 10 - Affirmation: _____

_____
_____
_____

Step 11 - Stand in Power Pose: Repeat the affirmation for 2 minutes, twice daily, with conviction while standing in a power pose. Smell *Believe*™ or *Transformation*™ Oil Blend as you do this. (You may choose another transforming oil if you'd like, such as *Build Your Dream*™, *Magnify Your Purpose*™, etc)

Repeat for *at least three consecutive days*, or until you create a new affirmation. Check off each box when complete.

Always make sure that your energy feels clear when you say the statement. If you experience inner resistance, use the AFT process to identify and release any negative thoughts, feelings, or memories that come up.

Date	AM	PM

Step 12 - Make Your Plan of Action: _____

_____
_____
_____
_____
_____
_____

Follow-up - What has changed in your life because of THIS Aroma Freedom Technique Session? _____

_____

_____

_____

_____

_____

_____

_____

_____

_____

_____

_____

_____

_____

_____

_____

_____

_____

_____

_____

Program your mind daily! As soon as one affirmation is complete or the goal has been reached, create another. Make affirmations a daily habit and soon you will not feel right unless you have done your daily practice. This will keep you focused in the direction of your dreams. Feel free to experiment with different oils as you progress.